HEALTH POLICY –
THE HARD WAY

Also by James E. Ludlam

Informed Consent

HEALTH POLICY –
THE HARD WAY

An Anecdotal Personal History
by One of the California Players

by JAMES E. LUDLAM

Hope Publishing House
Pasadena, California

Copyright © 1998 James E. Ludlam

For information address:
Hope Publishing House
P.O. Box 60008
Pasadena, CA 91116 - U.S.A.
Tel: (626) 792-6123 / Fax: (626) 792-2121
E-mail: hopepub@loop.com
Web site: http://www.hope-pub.com
Cover design — Michael McClary/The Workshop

Printed in the U.S.A. on acid-free paper

Library of Congress Cataloging-in-Publication Data

Ludlam, James E.
    Health policy--the hard way : an anecdotal personal history by one
of the California players / by James E. Ludlam.
        p.   cm.
    Includes index.
    ISBN 0-932727-94-8
    1. Medical policy -- California. 2. Medical care -- Law and legis-
lation -- California. 3. Hospitals -- Law and legislation -- California.
4. Insurance, Health -- Law and legislation -- California. I. Title
RA395.A4C277   1998
362.1'09794 -- dc21   98--14909
                                                              CIP

Table of Contents

Dedication

This book is dedicated to my partners and associates at Musick, Peeler & Garrett, whose loyalty, support and, above all, true professional dedication to the solution of healthcare problems made possible the projects reported in this book.

My special thanks go to my secretary Clara King, who has suffered through the many drafts of the chapters of this book and has been a constant interface with my clients and friends.

Steve Gamble, who volunteered to edit the product for both form and substance when I am sure he had much better things to do, has always been special as an adviser and cohort.

My wife Jane, since we first met in Munich, Germany, in 1938, has graciously put up with my idiosyncrasies as well as the many meetings I attended that are endemic to the healthcare decision-making process.

Last, but not least, I am grateful to the many healthcare leaders to whom we are all indebted for the continued progress in solving the increasingly complex problems of the cost, access and availability of healthcare.

Preface

Why this book? When I first mentioned to Chuck Forbes, my valued partner and co-participant in many of the events to be reported in this book, his response was, with a twinkle in his eye, "Is it an ego trip or do you really have something that you want to say?" Certainly that was a fair challenge to make this hopefully more than an ego trip. What I want to do is to record some anecdotes from my 57 years of personal experience in the health field, during what some of us old-timers like to describe as the golden age of medicine. It was a period when individual leaders of both hospitals and medicine had a tremendous impact on the quality and the availability of healthcare, particularly here in California where much of the action has occurred and continues to evolve.

In my judgment California enjoyed more than its share of leaders who served the state and the nation well in facing the problems and potentials of healthcare. The Depression, World War II and the unrest of the post-war period led to a major restructuring of our health system. It was a time when the potential needs for healthcare expanded more rapidly than the ability of our economy could respond in competition with other social needs. Unfortunately, healthcare is becoming more dehumanized – treated like a commodity. Some of the fun and satisfaction of participating in this evolutionary process have been wrung out of it as we are forced to shrink the system and ration care.

My greatest regret is that in the anecdotal approach of this volume I have been unable to give credit to many of the leaders in California's healthcare system who have made tremendous contributions to the positive results that have been achieved. At least I have attempted to report some of my personal experiences and pay tribute to some of the giants in the field with whom I was privileged to work. Hopefully I will have explained, in part, the genesis of these events and the lessons which may be learned from what we did. This book is also organized topically, each chapter addressing a separate subject rather than being a comprehensive historical review on a chronological basis.

During the historical period covered by this book, what is loosely called "the healthcare industry" evolved from being a collection of small enterprises consisting of a few doctors, generally practicing independently or in small groups identified with a local community hospital, to an industry that is a major factor in our expanding economy. Through the massive increase of demand created by major government programs such as Medicare and Medicaid coupled with the creation of health insurance and, more recently, managed care, this industry has become a threat to the financial stability of our federal government and equally to state and local governmental agencies as those entities face increasing budget deficits in financing or providing healthcare.

Furthermore the industry is burdened with being both capital- and people-intensive in its operating structure. Historically it was dedicated to community service, largely promoted by not-for-profit organizations. It has evolved into a complex hierarchy of bureaucratic layers that have added increased costs to the units of service and have distorted access and universal availability of its product.

I used to say that a hospital had every problem of a complex business entity, plus a medical staff which doubled its difficulties. In recent years the hospital has found itself partially phased out as the center of healthcare availability and healthcare policy decisions as managed care and fully integrated healthcare delivery systems take the place of hospital trustees and hospital executives as the critical decision-makers. Like no other major industry, the provision of healthcare is a complex matrix of continuous choices, starting with the individual seeking access to healthcare, whether to a pharmacy, a physician or any other healthcare provider. At this point there is triggered a whole series of options that will impact on the issues of access, cost and quality of care.

It is how some of these policy decisions were made that this book explores. An important issue is perceiving how everyone benefits, especially the patient, when all healthcare providers work together in a spirit of mutual trust. What has been unique to California is that during this "golden age of medicine" there has been an ability of the organized physician community and the institutional providers such as hospitals to work together in developing voluntary solutions in the best interest of patient care, as well as preventing a governmental takeover, which has been periodically proposed.

As I now look back over my many years of involvement in healthcare policy decisions, I can only marvel at the changes that have occurred as the healthcare field has astronomically expanded in size and complexity. Of equal importance, the entire economy has also expanded and the role of government has been increasingly invasive.

The problems of healthcare costs, quality and availability are overwhelming and increasingly involve outside forces, issues and emotions far beyond the ability of any small group of individuals, no matter how well intentioned, to resolve. As has long been true, problem solving is a matter of process and incremental decision-making. Unfortunately, in the health field it now appears that major changes can only occur when the public faces a major crisis in the satisfaction of its expectations from the system. Equally important, the consequences must impact what is roughly described as the great middle class.

My own role as a healthcare attorney has been in private general practice serving for extended periods as outside legal counsel to the California Hospital Association, the Hospital Council of Southern California, Blue Cross of Southern California, and many individual hospitals and healthcare entities as the practice of healthcare law evolved as a recognized specialty.

Timeline

Legislative Benchmarks

1935   Legislation regarding State Mandated Compulsory Health Insurance

1938   Incorporation of California Physicians Service

1945   • California Constitutional Amendment #13, Welfare Exemption Amendment – Property Tax Amendment for Charitable Organizations (hospitals etc.)

       • US Congress amended Federal Income Tax Law – Health Insurance not subject to income tax

1948   National Labor Relations Board ruled that the Provision of Health Insurance is subject to collective bargaining

1950   Legislature passes Minors Consent for Pregnancy Care Law

1953   California Amendment Bill strengthening tax-exempt status of hospitals

1954   General Election – California Constitutional Amendment expanding definition of tax-exempt status

1959   Good Samaritan Law adopted (exemption from liabilities)

1961   • Legislation for Immunity from liability passed

       • Adoption of state legislation regarding experience rating formula for hospitals

1966   • Passage of Title XIX (US) to the Social Security Act establishing Medicaid

       • Establishment by state legislature of MediCal

1968   Medical care & consents – legislation to permit minors (15 years or older) to consent to his/her own treatment

1969   California Constitutional Amendment adopted California Health Facility Construction Loan Insurance Law

1970 Adoption by State Legislature – Industry volunteer rating program adopted as proposed

1971 California Hospital Disclosure Act

1974 Section 1319, Health & Safety Code requiring every member of a medical staff to have professional liability insurance as a condition to being on the staff of a health facility

1975 Passage of MICRA – Medical Injury Compensation Reform Act

1977 California legislature extends laws governing consent treatment for minors (12 or older) relating to sexual assault, contagious or communicable diseases and drug/alcohol-related problems

1984 Legislation – Section 43.8 added to Civil Code providing immunity to individuals and organizations that provide information to peer review committees.

Legal Benchmarks

1941 State Commission ruled *against* tax-exempt status for hospitals and *for* hospital employee unemployment benefits

1944 California Supreme Court ruled in favor of hospitals, submitting strong opinions on the definition of charity – giving tax-exempt status to hospitals

1950 California Supreme Court ruled in favor of *Cedars of Lebanon v. County of Los Angeles* upholding the property tax exemption

1959 *Dr. Wyatt v. Tahoe Forest Hospital District* regarding physician staff membership

1964 *Rosner v. Peninsula Hospital District* – Court required medical staff member must carry malpractice insurance

1977 American Bar Association Report – Medical Professional Liability

1984 California Supreme Court upheld constitutionality of MICRA

1992 Case of *Rideout Hospital Foundation v. Yuba County* – District Court of Appeal upheld tax-exempt status

1995 US Supreme Court, *Allied-Bruce Terminix Co.s v. Dobson,* held that Federal Arbitration Act preëmpts state statutes

1996 California Supreme Court, *Arnett v. Dal Cielo* held the protection against discovery under 1157 did not apply to the State Medical Board in its investigation into possible physician misconduct

1

How it All Started: Unemployment Insurance for Hospitals

W hen friends ask how I ever got involved in the legal side of healthcare, the answer is very simple – pure luck.

On the afternoon of January 19, 1940, when I returned to the office of the seven-attorney law firm of Musick and Burrell as a newly minted and licensed attorney, having been admitted to the California Bar Association that morning, I was called to the office of Mr. Howard Burrell who instructed me to go to Seaside Memorial Hospital in Long Beach to see what could be done to help out Miss Ermela Witke, RN, the hospital administrator, who had called him that morning with a problem.

What I found in Long Beach was an ex-county hospital building, now housing a nonprofit acute-general hospital created primarily by a group of physicians in 1937. They had first organized it as a for-profit corporation and then converted it to a not-for-profit corporation. On its reorganization the hospital had applied for exemption from various state and federal tax and unemployment insurance contributions at both levels.

However, pending a ruling on its applications, the hospital had paid both federal and state unemployment insurance taxes. The particular problem which I was to address was that three nurses who had been terminated from employment had applied for unemployment insurance benefits of approximately $90 per week each. The hospital administrator was concerned the payment of benefits would adversely affect the tax-exempt status of the hospital. Also, Miss Witke wanted a refund on the unemployment insurance taxes paid since 1937.

The underlying issue was whether the hospital qualified for tax exemption under Section 7191 of the state unemployment insurance act which at that time exempted "a corporation, community chest, fund or foundation, organized and operated exclusively for religious, charitable, scientific, literary or educational purposes, or for the prevention of cruelty to children or animals, no part of the net earnings of which inures to the benefit of any private shareholder or individual."

From the viewpoint of the state, the issue narrowed down to whether or not a hospital which substantially relied upon the receipt of payment from pay patients could qualify as being "operated exclusively for charitable purposes." This struck at the fundamental basis for tax exemption of not-for-profit hospitals under a wide variety of tax statutes, including both state and federal corporate income taxes and qualification as a tax-exempt entity to receive charitable gifts.

From a practical point of view, I also discovered that the hospital did not have an accounting system that could support its legal contention. Back then, hospital accounting was based on cash flow, recording cash in and cash out. Charity care not being a cash item was not recorded or reported. In effect, uncollected accounts included what is now identified as charity care and no attempt was made to establish accounts receivable which were classified as charity care. They were just written off after an extended period.

Much of the charity work done in the hospital, such as free- or part-pay clinics and many health and educational programs, were not costed out or effectively recorded. The relationship between the hospital and its physicians was quite different from what we know today. The hospitals relied on voluntary services by physicians to care for indigent patients and no record was kept as to the volume or value of these voluntary services. "Robinhood medicine" was in vogue; physicians relied on the fees from pay patients to support their charity care. Health insurance was only a blip on the horizon and no other programs to pay for indigent care existed except as part of state and federal welfare programs.

Upon my assuming responsibility for the Seaside Memorial Hospital case there followed a series of administrative proceedings on the exempt status of the hospital. On February 7, 1941, the California Unemployment Insurance Commission ruled: 1) that the hospital was not entitled to exemption from the provisions of the act nor to any refund of past contributions, and 2) that hospital employees were entitled to unemployment benefits.

The next month, on behalf of the hospital, we applied to the Superior Court of Los Angeles County for a writ mandate to compel the commission to rule that the hospital was exempt and that payments previously made be refunded. Meanwhile the commission, in apparent reaction to these proceedings, revoked the unemployment insurance tax-exempt status of many of the major nonprofit hospitals in the state.

At the time there were few proprietary hospitals and these were primarily modest operations owned and operated by a small group of physicians as an extension of their medical practice. Thus the commission action came as a tremendous shock to most healthcare providers faced with the possibility of extended legal proceedings as well as back taxes.

I should point out that few not-for-profit hospitals at this time retained paid legal counsel. As a matter of practice each hospital relied upon volunteer legal service, generally by a prominent local attorney who served on its board of trustees just as many churches are served even now. Thus hospitals had outstanding legal talent who in fact knew little about, or had little experience with, special hospital problems such as this one.

Up to that time hospitals had experienced few legal entanglements. After its incorporation – a simple process – a typical hospital only needed what was then called a "Constitution and Bylaws" for its women's auxiliary and one for its medical staff, some consent forms – which it normally copied from another hospital – and some guidance on construction contracts. Since hospitals were not considered good financial risks, they relied on fund-raising to finance capital improvements and deficits, so there were none of the legal entanglements we know today with financing in the public marketplace. This was truly a cottage industry.

As hospitals were faced with threats to their tax-exempt status there was great concern this could also affect their exempt status under the tax laws which would seriously impact their fund-raising. Since our law office was the only one with any knowledge of the subject, we were asked to help hospitals throughout the state. Consequently I had the unique experience of going all over California to assist individual hospitals in their preparation of legal responses to the commission's action.

Due to the common lack of adequate financial records they all had difficulties developing the factual basis needed to support their position, so I became intimately acquainted with the internal operations of each hospital – an experience which proved of continued value to me as my healthcare legal practice expanded prior to the recognition of health law as a specialty.

The day for the Seaside Memorial Hospital hearing at the trial court was hanging fire when I traveled to Boston to marry Jane on September 27, 1941. On our honeymoon, driving across the country, I called the office from Winnemuca, Nevada, to find the hearing was scheduled for the following Monday. Our honeymoon was summarily terminated as we raced back to Los Angeles so I could prepare my oral argument.

Arriving in court Monday morning, I found the back of the room filled with volunteer attorneys representing other local hospitals. Other than the argument on the law relating to the tax exemption, the principal issues were factual. Prior to the hearing I had negotiated with the legal counsel for the commission an agreed statement of facts which was critical to the ultimate favorable result. In summary, it was agreed that the hospital treated both charity and pay patients, deriving a major portion of its revenues from pay patients.

The key agreement accepted by the attorney representing the commission was that the hospital facilities, including its emergency room, were available to any person without discrimination or ability to pay and that none of its revenues were received as profits by any individual. The judge ruled from the bench that the exemption should be recognized by the commission and that the relief requested was proper.

Similar proceedings were held in other courts following the same pattern. However, I was not on hand for these because with the outbreak of WW II, I was commissioned an ensign in the U.S. Navy and was off to active duty.

The California Employment Commission appealed and succeeded in obtaining a reversal of the trial court decision in the district court of appeals. However, the hospitals in turn moved for hearing in the California Supreme Court, which, in two separate opinions, *Scripps Memorial Hospital, Inc. v. California Employment Commission*, 24 C. 2d 669, and *Seaside Memorial Hospital of Long Beach v. California Employment Commission*, 24 C. 2d 681, both decided on August 18, 1944, ruled in favor of the hospitals in very strong opinions on the definition of charity. The court held that it was immaterial that such an institution is supported in part by full-pay or part-pay patients. It was the use to which any profit or income is devoted which is controlling. "Any person, the rich as well as the poor, may fall sick or be injured and become a fit subject for charity" (St. Luke Chapter 10, verses 30-37).

However, even with these decisions, the problems with the exempt status of nonprofit organizations did not go away as postwar labor unions shifted the attack on hospital charity exemption to the legislature. At each biennial legislative session, bills were introduced to repeal the exemption for all not-for-profit organizations. Upon my return from service it became my role, on behalf of the California Hospital Association, to organize a coalition of exempt institutions – such as the Community Chests, orphanages, colleges and universities – to defeat the proposals.

We were successful but we could see a gradual shrinking of our margin for victory. I therefore recommended to the board of trustees of the California Hospital Association that it review its position on this issue and decide whether or not the continued battle did more harm than good. If we moved to repeal just the unemployment insurance tax exemption for hospitals, we would successfully isolate the unemployment insurance tax issue from the other tax exemptions – which were far more critical to the not-for-profit hospitals.

As a practical matter the chief argument by the hospitals and other charity organizations was that by the nature of their operation they were not subject to the unemployment cycles of other major employers. There was little fluctuation in employment – not like the swings in the agricultural packing houses and the movie industry – and if hospitals were required to pay the approximate three percent payroll tax, it would only be contributing to those less stable employers as the tax was the same regardless of the individual employer experience. As the result of this policy review the CHA board decided that if the unemployment insurance tax as applied to hospitals were assessed in such a manner that each hospital would be taxed based on its own experience and not on the basis of the state employer pool, then the association would no longer object to lifting of the exemption for hospitals.

The next hurdle to surmount was that the state unemployment insurance tax was a part of a two-tiered tax created by the Roosevelt New Deal social security measures mandating a combination of state and federal taxes. No change could be made in the state tax, such as the proposed experience rating of hospitals, without action of the U.S. Congress amending the federal act to permit this result. We were further informed that the Congress only acted on amendments to the Federal Social Security Act about once every ten years and even then with great reluctance.

In any event I went to Sacramento and met with the assemblyperson who had always led the battle against us, John Burton from San Francisco. I suggested to him that legislation be adopted setting up the proposed experience-rating formula for hospitals but that the effective date for removing the exemption be deferred until appropriate action was taken by the U.S. Congress on the matter of experience rating. We agreed and the legislation was adopted, thus taking the heat off us at the state level.

Following adoption of the state legislation in 1961, our next problem was to get the American Hospital Association to take a neutral position on the changes we needed at the federal level to authorize states voluntarily to permit nonprofit organizations, including hospitals, to participate in the state unemployment insurance program on an institution-specific experience rating. I approached Dr. Ed Crosby, CEO of the AHA, for his support. He explained it was AHA Board policy to oppose any such action. I asked if the AHA would publish an article by me setting forth the California position. Thus the February 16, 1973, issue of *Hospitals* carried a five-page article entitled "Nonprofit Hospitals and Unemployment Insurance – Reexamination of a Basic Position." The editors of *Hospitals* included an extended rebuttal to my article which started:

> Mr. Ludlam believes that the Association's position on coverage of nonprofit hospitals under the federal unemployment insurance law is in error. We are happy to publish his dissent, but its publication should not be construed to imply a change in Association policy on the matter.

In spite of the AHA opposition, the necessary amendments to the federal Social Security Act were enacted and the voluntary experience-rated program we designed for California was made effective by the California Legislature some 30 years after the start of the case of Seaside Memorial Hospital (now the Memorial Hospital of Long Beach).

The 1970 legislation was designed by us to permit employers such as hospitals to establish self-funded liability pools and share administrative costs of the implementation of the insurance program in lieu of paying tax contributions to the state fund. The California Hospital Association established an extremely successful program to service member hospital needs for this purpose, further reducing the adverse economic impact on hospitals. This was definitely hospital policy change the hard way.

Although California hospitals did not take the lead on the legislative action to make possible the voluntary participation by not-for-profit organizations in the old age and survivors' insurance component of the Social Security Act, we fully supported this change and when it occurred, we strongly encouraged hospitals to elect to participate voluntarily. This was in line with our developing philosophy to support measures that would assure the availability of qualified and content hospital employees.

2

Blue Cross & Blue Shield

The history of healthcare in California cannot be fully understood without a basic explanation of the special roles Blue Cross and Blue Shield performed that went far beyond being the original third-party payors of healthcare on a prepaid basis. These two organizations evolved out of a cauldron of economic, social and political pressures in the 1930s. Many of the problems that led to their special roles and structures were far greater than the entities themselves. For example, some of the issues and conflicts that led to or arose out of their creation are still not completely resolved. Some of the most important concerns were:

- Should physicians and hospitals support the concept of health insurance through an indemnity mechanism or by the provision of service?
- Directly related to the above issue is whether or not a service plan constitutes the corporate practice of medicine, thus violating one of the primary concerns of organized

medicine of California.

- Should such hospital-based services as radiology and pathology, and later anesthesiology, be considered a hospital service to be covered by Blue Cross or a medical service covered by Blue Shield?
- Related to this, how should radiologists and pathologists be compensated?
- The division of Blue Cross into multiple plans with a separate statewide physician plan.
- Should health insurance be available to all employees or should there be an income cap?
- Use of community premium rating for health insurance.
- Insurance reimbursement to hospitals on a per diem, retail billing or cost plus.
- Should health insurance be mandated by the state or should it be voluntary?
- Who should regulate the Blue plans and, if so, what should be the degree of regulation?
- The governance structure of the service plans and the degree of physician and/or hospital control.
- The role of and conflict between the AMA and the CMA respectively in regard to health policy in California.
- What is to be considered "socialized medicine"?
- Coverage for spouse or dependents.
- Is pregnancy a planned event and therefore uninsurable?

All of this was played out during the depression period from 1929 to the advent of World War II. It was a time of mutual tension between physicians and hospitals that can best be described as "survival." Thus one of the stated concerns of physicians was the fact that substantially all hospitals required a cash deposit at time of admission, whereas the physician was often the last debtor to be paid by a patient, if at all.

As Howard (Hap) Hassard, the legal architect acting on behalf of both CMA and Blue Shield, reported in his reminiscences, an oral history entitled "Fifty Years in Law and Medicine" when asked to explain why the physician community seriously considered mandatory health insurance: "They were hungry."

Now when we discuss the critical problems of healthcare access and affordability in the mid-1990s I can only say—you don't know what trouble is unless you were here in the 1930s. There was no commercial insurance. Development of the Blue Plans was just evolving in those days.

The first plans were essentially single hospital plans, created initially for the benefit of their own hospital employees with gradual expansion into the community. There were at least six such plans in California initiated by hospitals, but limited to hospital care, not physician care—which was often volunteered.

On the physician side, some activity came out of the Alameda County Medical Association which in 1933 proposed to the CMA at its annual meeting that the CMA sponsor the creation of a voluntary hospital prepayment plan. The house of delegates rejected the proposal but this gave rise to a strong movement within the CMA to develop a compulsory health insurance scheme and a committee of six was appointed to develop such a plan.

This was Howard Hassard's initiation to top medical association policy and politics. He later went on to be such an important and constructive leader in the field of legal medicine, not only as the ultimate legal counsel to the CMA; he even acted as its executive director for a period. It was Hap who staffed the committee of six which presented the proposal for a state mandated compulsory health insurance plan to the CMA House of Delegates in 1935. Amazingly, it was approved and then submitted to the Legislature for action.

At the 1935 legislative hearings the CMA proposal was opposed by the chamber of commerce, organized labor and the press, all of whom emphasized that it did too much for the physician community. The proposal was defeated and at the 1936 session of the CMA House of Delegates, support switched back to the concept of a voluntary health insurance plan. Legislation was introduced in 1937 to implement such a plan but it, too, was defeated.

With the end of the Republican governorship and election of

Culbert Olson as governor—who publicly stated he would introduce his own health insurance plan—a new incentive was created for action by the CMA, which was determined to go ahead without legislation at the 1938 meeting of its house of delegates. CMA's decision was to incorporate the "California Physicians' Service" as a nonprofit corporation, which placed it under the supervision of the attorney general—not the insurance commissioner.

The CMA House of Delegates action in 1938 was in spite of the efforts of Dr. Morris Fishbein, leader of the American Medical Association (AMA). He opposed any form of health insurance and sent out his chief deputy to lobby the members of the CMA House of Delegates against favoring any health insurance program. The vote was overwhelmingly in support except for four votes from the Sacramento delegation who backed an indemnity insurance program rather than a service plan—an issue which continues to be controversial. On the other hand, the CMA leadership believed an indemnity program would not be adequate to defeat Governor Olson's proposal.

The newly incorporated plan of 1939 had important characteristics that adversely affected future attempts to merge the Blue Cross Plan with the Blue Shield Plan—a logical combining which has occurred in nearly every other state. Under the California Blue Shield corporate setup there were three classes of members. The professional members who were participants in the plan on payment of a five-dollar registration fee and which was open to all physicians whether or not they were members of CMA. The second type were the subscriber members who purchased health service from the company. The third class were the administrative members, 75 in number, initially all physicians chosen locally.

The administrative membership group was the control group who elected the board of directors and had the corporate member legal authority. Actually, the concept did not work too effectively because of the difficulty of achieving a quorum. Members had to pay their own travel expense, and plane travel was quite limited in those days. After three years the plan was amended to make the members of the CMA House of Delegates the administrative members because they could act at the annual or other meetings of the CMA House of Delegates without quorum concerns. Ultimately this class was changed to be designated as corporate members with fifty percent physicians and fifty percent subscribers.

The Blue Shield Plan was limited to individuals who had less than $3,000 annual income. Member physicians were required to accept the Blue Shield fee schedule as full payment for any services. Any physician who was not a member of the plan could bill the patient for the difference between what Blue Shield paid and the standard fee of the physician – giving a strong incentive for the subscriber to choose a plan physician.

From the physicians' viewpoint there was the uncertainty of being paid on a *unit* basis out of a pool. The *unit* was an arbitrary measure of participation and not nearly as sophisticated as the "relative value scale" ultimately developed by CMA for use by all health insurers. Although Blue Shield subscriber premiums were relatively low at $2.50 per month, the program was hard to sell, as the concept of prepaid insurance was not understood by the public. Also, since the premium level was initially so low, the physicians' unit return started at only 50 percent of billed charges and for several years fell even below that until Blue Shield achieved broader acceptance.

At the same time this activity was occurring on the CMA side there was considerable activity on the hospital side to develop hospital insurance. Much of the support for a hospital plan actually came from physicians who supported this, not only as a public good but also in the belief that if patients had hospital insurance their ability and desire to pay the physicians' bills would be greatly improved.

Thus regional Blue Cross plans developed in three parts of the state. To some extent these emerged as expansions of the single hospital plans previously discussed. The first regional plan was created in 1932 by R.D. Brisbane, superintendent at Sutter Hospital in Sacramento, and included in addition to this hospital, the Mercy General Hospital (originally the Sisters Hospital) and the Woodland Medical Group. This was named the Superior California Hospital Association and later renamed the Intercoast Hospitalization Insurance Association when it qualified as a Blue Cross Plan. Initially it was incorporated as a nonprofit corporation and was quite successful. The plan expanded up and down the Central Valley. Eventually it gave up its Blue Cross status and converted to a disability insurer with other lines of insurance.

In the San Francisco Bay Area the activity was led by those progressives in the Alameda County Medical Association who had initiated the action within CMA. In 1934 they created the East Bay Mutual Hospital Association that was later converted into Blue Cross of Northern California. Its heritage of Medical Society initiation gave this plan a strong bias to the physician side in its future development as distinguished from the hospital leadership in the Southern California plan. This thereafter became a major source of conflict between the two plans.

In Southern California the Los Angeles County Medical Association was controlled by classic fee-for-service physicians who strongly opposed prepaid service health insurance contracts. As evidence of its bias the association in 1934 expelled both Doctors Ross and Loos of the Ross-Loos Medical Group for allegedly soliciting patients and engaging in contract practice. Probably this action was a blessing to Ross-Loos as that medical group continued to grow and prosper from its original affiliation with Queen of the Angels Hospital, through building its own hospital directly across the Hollywood Freeway from "Queen" and later being acquired by CNA as a part of the movement to managed care in the late 1980s.

Blue Cross in Southern California grew out of the leadership of the regional hospital trade association, the Hospital Council of Southern California, particularly from Rollin France, superintendent of Golden State Hospital, Ritz Heerman, chief executive of Lutheran Hospital, and Monsignor T.J. O'Dwyer, head of hospitals and charities for the archdiocese of Los Angeles. They organized Associated Hospital Service of Southern California under the new provisions of the California Insurance Code, Chapter 11A, commencing with Section 11491 of Part 2 of Division 2, as adopted by the Legislature in 1937.

As a part of this movement, these leaders who were working on development of regional hospital service plans organized the formation of the Association of California Hospitals (ACH), later renamed the California Hospital Association (CHA), as the first statewide hospital trade association. Formerly state politics had been handled by the Association of Western Hospitals, which had a section for California hospitals. Western was primarily dedicated to educational programs coupled with an annual meeting held every other year in California and on alternate years in the other western states.

As distinguished from the physician-based organization in the north that was seeking to avoid regulation and assure physician control, the hospital leaders in Southern California accepted the concept of supervision by the commissioner of insurance and the concept that the board of directors would be made up of one-third representatives of contracting hospitals, one-third physicians and one-third representatives of the public – all of whom were elected as board members by a constituency from the contracting hospitals or the hospital regional trade associations. Under the statute, the California Department of Public Health had authority to issue a certificate of approval to qualified hospitals plus the responsibility for hearing appeals from denials of a contract by individual hospitals seeking one.

Although the Association of California Hospitals attempted to create a single state hospital plan, this failed, so the three plans proceeded on their own, each following its own pattern of benefits as well as method of paying for hospital services.

Thus the Northern California Plan paid a hospital its full charges for its enrollees and provided hospital service benefits for 21 days of hospitalization with exclusions for treatment of cancer, tuberculosis, venereal disease, mental disorders, self-inflicted injuries and pregnancy. The initial premium was 90 cents per month and was limited to employed individuals between the ages of 18 and 65 – with no dependent coverage. Radiology and pathology coverage was provided on an indemnity basis to avoid the corporate practice of medicine problem. The enrollment of employees was a new concept and the employers initially refused to make payroll deductions or contribute to the premium; thus an employee had to volunteer to collect the monthly premiums from fellow employees – an administrative nightmare. In any case, group enrollment was essential to avoid adverse selection.

In Southern California, hospital participation was solicited to provide hospitalization at an all-inclusive rate of eight dollars a day for the first ten days, with six dollars per day for the next eleven for a total of a 21-day maximum. The exclusions were essentially the same as in the north, but a twelve-day maternity benefit was included. Radiology, pathology and anesthesia were not covered. Groups of five to twenty employees required 100 percent enrollment, with family enrollment optional. The individual monthly premium for a group of over 25 employees with at least 60 percent enrolled was 75 cents per month. For less than 60 percent the premium was 85 cents per month. The southern plan was successful in having some major employers make payroll deductions, but they did not make any company contributions to the premium. This rate structure lasted only a short while until it became necessary to surcharge groups which had a record of over-utilization.

Current reports of managed care reduction of maternity benefits for normal deliveries to one or two days call to mind that in my research for this chapter I came across a report that Dr. August Hromadka, then owner of the Santa Monica Hospital, was so concerned about the practice of limiting the number of covered days of payment for the hospitalization period of maternity patients that his hospital provided free hospitalization for an additional four days for any patient who would stay over ten days.

During this early period there was a major conflict in healthcare circles as to the legal right of a county hospital to provide care to non-indigent patients and to charge for such services. This was a hot issue in the rural areas of the state where the private hospitals objected to the practice. On the other hand some county boards of supervisors took the view that since county hospitals were built with taxpayer funds, the taxpayers should have the right to access such facilities for any care, not just that required for public health needs, emergencies or indigents.

A suit was brought against the Kern County Board of Supervisors challenging their practice of open access. In the famous case of *Goodall v. Brite*, 11 Cal. App. 2d 540, the district court of appeal in January 1936 ruled that this practice violated the state constitution as an improper use of county government funds. This rule remained in effect until modified in part when the Legislature established MediCal in 1966; this broadened the powers of county hospitals to care for private patients. At best the *Goodall* decision resolved a serious conflict between the public and private sectors, although recent litigation in Ventura County has again raised this issue.

Membership in both Blue Cross and Blue Shield plans expanded modestly until World War II mainly because of the lack of enthusiasm of employers. The war economy changed this. In 1942 the War Labor Board placed a national wage and price freeze to control inflation inherent in the massive war effort, but the next year this same board ruled that the provision of health insurance was exempt from the wage freeze. This was a major concession to the defense contractors, who were in a strong position to pass these costs on to the federal government. As a result there was a major surge in enrollment and Philo Nelson, president of Blue Cross of Northern California, reported his paid solicitors were climbing all over the fuselage of airplanes under construction to sign up workers.

Then in 1945 the Congress, in amending the federal income tax law, provided for the first time that health insurance was not subject to income tax by the individual employee if the insurance was provided by the employer. Again, this was a great incentive to the provision of health insurance by employers. Three years later, to complete the picture, the National Labor Relations Board ruled that the provision of health insurance was subject to collective bargaining, which meant an employer could be held for bad faith for refusing to bargain over health insurance.

Before moving on to the developments in national health insurance, I should note that when the hospitals in Southern California established what was to become the Associated Hospital Service of Southern California in March of 1938, the original payment to hospitals was a flat four dollars per day for inpatient admission. The board of directors became concerned that this method did not fairly reflect the differences in individual hospital programs and costs and so converted to a cost-plus-five-percent approach. This required a system of uniform accounting and cost finding that was spelled out in the hospital agreement with Blue Cross. As we will see, this became a matter of national significance.

After the founding of Blue Shield in 1939, both the Northern and Southern Blue Cross plans had joint-marketing agreements with Blue Shield to cover physician services while the Blue Cross plans paid for hospital services. This agreement was important in attracting national accounts that were negotiated by other plans throughout the country, but it created acute internal friction as conflicts developed between the hospital and physician plans as to how the premium dollar should be split. Finally in 1942 the Northern Blue Cross plan withdrew from the joint approach and for the first time offered a complete package including both hospital and physician services. In 1950 the Southern plan also terminated its agreement with Blue Shield.

In 1949 the Northern Blue Cross plan entered into an agreement with the Alameda County Medical Society under which the society established a review process to reconsider Blue Cross claims that were denied for admissions that did not seem to be necessary for patient care. This early form of utilization control soon spread to other counties throughout the state.

By the next year there were 600,000 Blue Cross members in the South and 500,000 members in the North – but major competition was developing with the new commercial health insurance plans being marketed by most major life insurance carriers. Initially the Southern plan did not recognize brokers but dealt directly with employers and individual subscribers. By the late 1950s the competition was so intense and so many major employers' placement of insurance was controlled by brokers that the Southern plan followed the Northern plan's lead and recognized brokers.

When Howard Burrell died in 1953 I succeeded him as general counsel to the California Hospital Association and also as general counsel, board member and secretary to the board of directors of Hospital Service of Southern California (Blue Cross Plan of Southern California). I served in that capacity for the next 28 years.

Health insurance was not included in the Franklin D. Roosevelt New Deal programs, although there was continued expansion of federal involvement in funding healthcare for the needy as the states sought help in financing their responsibility in this area of welfare. This took the form of direct grants to the states rather than as employer- or individual-mandates for health insurance, but it was part of an evolving welfare system. Politically, in the 1950s there was continued pressure for some form of national health insurance. In California the slogan of both the CMA and CHA was "mainstream medicine" for the indigent rather than a demand for universal health insurance.

With the election of John F. Kennedy as president in 1959, coupled with a Democratic Congress, there was general expectation by the hospital and medical communities for some form of universal health coverage in America. The issue was who was to be covered, how it was to be financed and the role of the states.

Here in California the board of directors of CHA worked with our friends at Blue Cross for the answer to these questions. The individuals with the greatest need were obviously those on welfare. Our studies found that the population group with the least need was the elderly, while the newly married with children had serious problems as to the cost and availability of health insurance. Even though diverted by such problems as the Bay of Pigs, President Kennedy was working to develop his plan for universal health insurance when he was assassinated.

With the succession of Lyndon Johnson to the presidency the political atmosphere in Washington took a sudden shift towards action on welfare and health reform, including the war on poverty and the development of Titles XVIII and XIX to the Social Security laws; these later became known as the Medicare and Medicaid programs. Johnson, unwilling to risk defeat on a universal health insurance bill, opted to emphasize the care for those over age 65. After all, this group had far more votes than the poor and the children whom we in California sought to protect.

Although I have no way to prove it, it was and still is my opinion that Johnson's staff developed the Medicaid provisions as a *quid pro quo* to California for congressional support of Medicare. There was no full understanding as to the potential costs of the

Health Policy – The Hard Way

Medicaid program as it was designed. As I recall, the estimate then was that Medicaid might cost the federal government as much as five billion dollars annually, certainly nothing to compare with the present budget-busting results.

California hospitals' leadership were deeply apprehensive about the potentials of Medicare and especially how hospitals would be compensated. Particularly we worried that there might be a level fee schedule approach that would favor low-income states in the South as was provided in the post-war Hill-Burton fund allocations. There was also a split in the hospital industry. Although we in California were particularly concerned with hospital payments under the Medicare program, eastern hospitals, which tended to be better protected financially with endowments, were not as anxious about reimbursement under the Medicare program – they tended to treat anything they got as a windfall.

We sought to press for our Blue Cross cost-based reimbursement formula and worked with Senator Thomas Kuchel's staff to support this approach. He enjoyed a particularly critical committee appointment to help us. During Easter week of 1965 Sam Tibbitts, who has succeeded Ritz Heerman at the California Hospital and Lutheran Hospital Society, was in Chicago as a trustee of the American Hospital Association. He was seeking AHA support of the Southern California Blue Cross cost-based formula for hospital reimbursement plus a two percent additional nursing cost factor adjustment to cover the added cost of nursing care for the elderly. These changes had been determined by the Commission on Administrative Services to Hospitals (CASH), a program of the Hospital Council of Southern California.

I should explain the evolution of the CASH program. Developed by Samuel Tibbitts during his 1961-1962 presidency of the Hospital Council of Southern California, it was a specialized service to improve hospital operating efficiency and reduce costs. Sam believed that true principles of industrial engineering could be applied effectively to a service industry such as hospitals in the same manner as in the manufacturing industry with substantial beneficial cost reduction results. In coöperation with Blue Cross he developed a demonstration project at his California Lutheran Hospital in Los Angeles to establish work studies and standards on the performance of routine hospital tasks in a cost-effective manner. In one of these studies of performance of nurses the CASH engineers determined that nurses were required to spend seven percent more time performing the same service to patients over 65 than to younger patients. This factored out as an overall two percent additional cost per patient for those over 65.

The Hospital Council's executive, John Brewer, and I awaited word from Chicago that Sam had received the AHA Board support of the cost reimbursement formula. When the call from Sam came, John Brewer and I dashed to the Los Angeles airport, got a plane to Chicago where we met up with Sam and flew on to Washington, D.C., where Congress was about to act on the Medicare reimbursement formula. What we had not anticipated was that because it was Easter week, children and their families were coming to Washington for the cherry blossoms. Hotels were sold out and we could not get a place to stay in the city and it was already getting dark.

Finally we rented a car and headed out the Beltway to look for a motel but with little luck – although one place offered to rent us rooms for two hours. We ended up in Maryland and somehow got on a back road at about midnight when we got a flat tire. Piling out, we opened the trunk to discover the car had no jack. Just at that moment a Maryland state trooper flashed his floodlight on us demanding to know what we were up to. After our explanation he immediately got a jack out of his trunk, quickly changed our tire and using his radio located a place for us to stay to get a good rest for our next day on the Hill.

Our lobbying effort was successful and appropriate language

was inserted in the committee report, supporting cost-based reimbursement and the two-percent nursing adjustment. This modification saved the bacon for a lot of hospitals and lasted until HCFA shifted to DRG formula for hospital reimbursement in the mid-80s.

With the 1966 passage of Title XIX to the Social Security Act establishing the national Medicaid program, there was immediate pressure to implement state-by-state participation. Under the legislative design of Medicaid the federal government would share on a 50/50 basis with the state the cost of a complex program for healthcare for the medically indigent. There was a basic mandatory set of benefits the state was required to provide plus a broad spectrum of optional benefits the state could provide and still receive federal matching funds. As mentioned, this was the program both the CMA and CHA had sought to implement under the banner of "mainstream medicine" and meant our thrust would be to maximize the state participation in providing the optional benefits.

As soon as President Johnson signed the legislation authorizing Medicaid we were in contact with California Governor Pat Brown and his administration to draft the state participating legislation. The vehicle was AB 5 by Assemblyperson Jack Casey of Bakersfield. Paul Ward, secretary for health and welfare, representing the governor, and Chuck Stewart, his deputy, were the chief negotiators with Mr. Hassard and Mr. Willett acting on behalf of CMA and Blue Shield and Bill Whelan and myself representing CHA and Blue Cross. The result was a piece of legislation with broad eligibility provisions and a spectrum of benefits almost equal to Medicare, so we really did achieve mainstream medicine for the indigent.

The issue of administering these new entitlements was of great importance and CMA and CHA were strongly supportive of the use of the Blues to govern the program, particularly since the Blue plans were also involved in handling Medicare under Title XVIII. This approach was approved and the same negotiating team immediately proceeded to design contract provisions for a joint venture by Blue Cross and Blue Shield to manage the new plan. Because of our experience of working with Chuck Stewart it was agreed he should leave the state position to head up the joint venture. Chuck did an outstanding job and ultimately became the CEO of Blue Shield. Unfortunately, he was stricken with cancer and we lost him in 1995. Paul Ward, another key member of the state's team, continued in several different governmental roles until he was chosen to succeed Bill Whelan as president and CEO of CHA.

Looking back on the past 30 years of experience with MediCal (as we named the state program) it would appear that maybe we did too well in designing a mainstream plan. It became more than the state could afford, which has led to major cuts in both eligibility and benefits as both the state and federal government budget scarcities became acute.

Our mainstream concept included the use of private physicians on a limited fee-for-service basis. However, many physicians were reluctant to take MediCal patients as long as they had an adequate demand from private patients. Then with the advent of managed care and the competition from HMOs and PPOs we found no difficulty recruiting private physicians to serve Medicaid patients.

By the early 1990s, in administering an O.B.-access program established by the National Health Foundation, we were threatened with legal action for refusal to include certain physicians in a plan that would pay only MediCal rates – definitely a switch from times past when there was a grave reserve for successful physicians to participate in care of the indigent. With contracts for administering both Medicare and MediCal, the size of Blue Cross plans suddenly doubled so that in 1969 the three California Blues processed nearly 4.5 million claims for beneficiaries.

In 1970 Philo Nelson retired as president of Blue Cross North, succeeded by George C. Lucia, a longtime executive with the plan. Two years later H. Charles Abbott retired as president of Blue

Cross of Southern California and was followed by William A. Guy, who was recruited from a Midwestern plan. These changes came at a time when a cycle of cost-crunch pressures were developing in the total economy, and particularly in the health field where the cost surge was more than double the general inflation rate. As a result there were major efforts by employers and the government to control healthcare costs. Blue Cross plans were caught in the middle between the purchasers of health insurance on the one hand and the providers on the other.

All of this was in turn complicated by the medical malpractice insurance crisis that developed in the early 1970s, reaching a peak in the summer of 1975 when there was a substantial withdrawal of services by physicians in protest to the increase in malpractice insurance premiums. The resulting Medical Injury Compensation Reform Act legislation will be discussed later in this story. In response to these events Blue Cross and Blue Shield withdrew from the administration of MediCal, which became a state-administered program. At the same time the two Blue Cross Plans (but initially not Blue Shield) each initiated its own HMO as an alternative to fee-for-service medicine. In 1974 Blue Cross South purchased a 32-acre site in Woodland Hills and constructed a twelve-story building for a 1977 move-in. This is currently the location of the plan.

During this period a pattern of periodic discussions about merging the two Blue Cross Plans and Blue Shield continued. For a while it looked as though there would actually be a merger between Blue Cross South and Blue Shield, leaving out Blue Cross North because of its anti-Blue Shield attitude. Then in 1982 when Bill Guy retired as president of Blue Cross South and George Lucia retired as president of Blue Cross North, for the first time there was a real opportunity to merge the two Blue Cross plans. This was finalized in July 1982 with the selection of Daniel L. Smith as president of a combined Blue Cross of California.

Meanwhile the State Legislature had taken two significant

actions promoted by Bill Guy. The first, AB 789, authorized fixed-price prospective contracting with selected hospitals to provide care for MediCal patients. Second, under a parallel concept, AB 3480 was passed, authorizing all private insurers including Blue Cross to contract with hospitals at negotiated rates and offer incentives to consumers to use the contracting providers.

These two measures which introduced the concept of limiting access to selected contract providers who were chosen on a bid basis – not a cost-based – reimbursement, effectively abolished the original Blue Cross concept of assuring the patient free choice of both hospital and physician providers. This was true marketplace competition in the health field and caused Blue Cross to suffer financially for a time. It was not until well into the administration of Leonard D. Schaeffer as president, starting in 1986, that Blue Cross achieved its new major role in the healthcare market as a managed-care plan.

Now we look forward to a future in which the issue of limiting freedom of choice by patients of their hospital and, more importantly, their physicians, is no longer a line drawn in the sand – except for Medicare beneficiaries, who are rapidly becoming the last major group with guaranteed access to fee-for-service medicine. They still have a true freedom of choice – but one that will soon disappear under the pressures for cost control and the universal spread of managed care.

Freedom of choice as a concept was a partial substitute for "quality assurance;" since quality was to be assured, patients would choose to go to the better quality physicians and hospitals. Now the managed-care plans, such as HMOs and PPOs, have the burden of creating and implementing substitute quality assurance controls to protect the public from decisions made by employers in purchasing employee health insurance coverage.

Even with all of the changes in the structure of both Blue Cross and Blue Shield, they continue to play important leadership roles in the evolution of healthcare policy in both the legislature and the marketplace. For more than 40 years I have been dedicated to a merger of these two so they could speak as one voice for total healthcare. With recent shifts in the power structure of healthcare providers their role as the intermediary between the providers on the one hand and the purchasers of healthcare, both government and employers, on the other is being challenged by the rapid shift to the provision of care by the integrated delivery systems.

Hospitals are combining into systems and the physicians into large medical groups, both of which are continuing to flow into integrated delivery systems. These in turn seek to eliminate or challenge intermediaries such as the Blues by direct contracting with the newly evolving combinations of healthcare purchasers such as CalPers, on behalf of government employees in California, the affiliated employers groups such as Pacific Employers Group based in San Francisco on behalf of major employers, and HPSC, a state-sponsored program for small employers. What is now called direct contracting is a real threat to the Blue Plans and the health insurance companies, who must justify their share of the healthcare dollar that does not go to patient care.

I must pay personal tribute to H. Charles Abbott, who became president of Blue Cross South in 1954. A unique leader dedicated to solving the problems of cost, quality, availability and access to healthcare by all individuals, Charles was completely self-effacing but a tower of strength and support for all the constructive actions taken during his tenure by groups like the Hospital Council of Southern California and the California Hospital Association. Whenever we faced a new challenge, the first question was always, "What does Charles think?" Furthermore, he followed up his ideas with quiet action. The governing board and staff he recruited for his Blue Cross plan became the breeding ground for ideas and action that were a unique force for constructive health policy.

3

The Public Health League

During my apprenticeship days in the legislative arena in the 1940s I was assigned by Howard Burrell, legal counsel to CHA, to attend the occasional meetings of the Public Health League, an organization created by the California Medical Association to mobilize legislative support or opposition to legislation of interest to the allied health professions, made up essentially of doctors, dentists, hospitals and veterinarians.

Veterinarians were included in this group because, historically, schools of veterinary science have been closely associated with schools of medicine. Not only is there an overlap in the educational components but also the veterinary resources supply animals and research materials for the medical schools. I soon found out that from a legislative action point of view veterinarians were more important to legislators than were the hospitals for the simple reason that nearly every state senator in those days was from a farming background and had his own veterinarian just as he had

using doctors to lobby voters

his own family doctor or dentist. The key to legislative action in the health policy area was through the one-on-one relationship to the individual legislator through his own family physician, dentist and veterinarian.

The hospital network was not nearly as effective and our hospital problems were treated as low priority. In those days political action committees and other major fund-raising structures did not exist. The operation known as the Public Health League was run by Ben Read, a full-time lobbyist in Sacramento with offices in the Senator Hotel.

The Public Health League concentrated its activities on the public health committees in the Senate and Assembly and in the days of Ben Read it was a tremendous force. As a matter of fact, before the Brown Act and other pressures for open public meetings the Senate public health committees would meet in Ben Read's suite at the Senator Hotel for lunch to go over the committee agenda and get the votes all lined up before holding the formal public session.

In those days it was a lot easier for a committee under a powerful chairperson to keep things under control. Committee meetings were held in the old capitol buildings, around a long floor-level table behind a railing. Without adequate speaking amplification, if you were not in the front row of the visitors' section you had little chance of knowing what was going on.

Minutes were taken as directed by the chair, who could call for an oral vote and then announce how the vote went without a roll call. The speaker of the Assembly or the chairperson *pro tem* of the Senate controlled the assignment to committee of any particular piece of legislation – an action which often swayed the fate of a controversial piece of legislation. As has always been true, a majority favorable vote of the total committee was required for a "do pass." A committee member who did not want to be recorded as voting against a bill could just disappear.

During the period of legislative activity there could be three or four bills working in several widely separated committee locations. The key to success to get your votes was to be present, which meant you had to race between committee rooms. Meetings were scheduled morning, noon and night, with the floor session of each house scheduled separately, either morning or afternoon. We used to go up on the night train to Sacramento and assemble in the club car with other lobbyists to swap war stories or even negotiate compromises, then spend the day racing around the halls, hoping that any evening committee meeting would end in time for us to catch the night train back to Los Angeles.

It was always a hassle to get to the station. I will never forget the night we all raced out of the capitol building to catch cabs. Unfortunately, Monsignor O'Dwyer had left his luggage at the hotel so he came on alone, reaching the station just as the train pulled out. He had his cab chase the train down the valley some 30 miles to the next stop where the cab parked in front of the engine so he could get aboard.

This was before the essentially full-time legislature came into being, so the sessions were much shorter and, as a result, much more concentrated during the time the Legislature was in session. In spite of these pressures, representing hospitals was a gratifying activity and we were treated with respect.

Normally our strategy was to present witnesses to testify who knew the legislators in their district. I avoided testifying as much as possible, particularly before the judiciary committees, which were made up almost entirely of lawyers who took great pleasure in cutting up any attorney who appeared before them. In those days the Catholic sisters wore their full starched habits and were always received with special consideration. When I could, I always included a sister on our witness list.

I will never forget one hearing before the Assembly labor committee to which I had asked Sister Laurencita from the Holy

Cross Hospital in Fresno to testify. We came into the committee room and found there was a bill on the docket involving long-shoremen. The unions had brought in bus loads of dock workers to fill the visitors' gallery, so there was no seat for Sister Laurencita. I asked a longshoremen in the front row if he would give up his seat for her, which he graciously did. She no more than sat down when a union photographer rushed in to take pictures of the great turnout they had organized, so the union papers ran a picture the next day with sister sitting primly in her lovely habit in the midst of a burly group of dock workers. Being from a labor family, she fortunately was highly amused by it all.

With the advent of the new capitol office building the atmosphere of committee activities changed. The new chambers allowed the members to sit in a rising semi-circular forum for big committee procedures or on a raised dais in smaller committee gatherings. Each member had a microphone with the proceedings recorded for posterity. The chairperson definitely had less authority to manipulate the proceedings, although some still do pretty well.

Political action committees and various reforms in the legislative process have caused the Public Health League to fade away.

4

Consent to Treatment

In the 1940s and 1950s medical malpractice was just beginning to develop as a major issue for healthcare providers, particularly physicians. Nonprofit hospitals were essentially exempt from liability and the practice of medicine was far less complex than it later became. However, there was one problem that seriously concerned both hospitals and physicians – patient consent. The plaintiff's bar was not highly organized or specialized. Nearly any lawyer felt qualified to bring a lawsuit for failure of a healthcare provider to have a valid consent for treatment. Furthermore, a treatment without consent was regarded as battery with the possibility of being considered a crime. Violation was easy to prove and the consequences quite serious at the hands of a jury.

As a result the one subject that could attract an audience of physicians, nurses and medical record librarians was a discussion of the law of consents, particularly as related to that by minors who had no legal right to approve treatment. At that time 21 was the legal age of consent for most purposes, for in California the age of majority was not reduced to 18 years until 1971. Of great concern to physicians was the fact that the lack-of-consent issue was not limited to incompetent practitioners, but in actual practice some leading practitioners were held liable for large recoveries.

Various legislative approaches were adopted in an effort to resolve identified problems without reducing the age of consent from 21 to 18 because this would cause a change in the election laws – deemed to be sacred. However, at nearly every session of the Legislature we faced a new problem to be solved by legislative action and the question was assigned to me for solution.

One of the first exceptions was adoption of Section 25.5 to the civil code which would authorize a minor who was 17 years of age to consent to the donation of his or her blood and to the penetration of tissue which is necessary to accomplish such donation. In 1961, Section 25.6 of the civil code was adopted; it permitted any minor who had contracted a lawful marriage to consent to the furnishing of hospital, medical and surgical care, and further provided that for the purpose of this section only, a dissolution of marriage shall not remove such person's adult status once attained.

By 1968 Section 74.6 was adopted, which permitted minors 15 years of age or older living separate and apart from their parents or legal guardian, regardless of the duration of such separate residence, and who are managing their own financial affairs, regardless of the source of income, to give consent to hospital care and related medical procedures. This was known as the law of emancipation and was a headache for hospitals and physicians, but it provided a solution to many difficult situations even though it released the parent or guardian from financial responsibility if used. Also that year a minor twelve or older who might have come in contact with any infectious, contagious or communicable disease could consent to diagnosis and treatment for such exposure.

In 1961, by Section 25.7 of the civil code, a minor on active duty with the armed services was authorized to consent to the furnishing of hospital, medical or surgical care. By 1965 the law was clarified (Section 25.8) to permit either parent to give the consent. In 1977, Section 34.9 of the civil code extended such authorization to diagnosis and treatment related to sexual assault and through Section 34.10 the consent by twelve-year-olds or older was extended to permit care for drug- or alcohol-related problems.

All of the above changes were made quite easily and were implemented immediately to solve the obvious situations at hand. However, one amendment which I put through became quite controversial. In 1950, on behalf of the United Way and its welfare planning council, I was appointed chair of the Citizens Adoption Committee of Los Angeles County to encourage legal adoptions and to discourage what were described as black-market adoptions.

After one meeting of the committee, Sister Thomasine, head of Holy Family Adoption Agency, asked for my help in solving a problem for that agency. They were concerned about the many pregnant young girls who, unmarried, had fled their homes, often from out of state, as soon as they realized they were pregnant. Holy Family provided housing and counseling to them up to the time for delivery, at which point it was necessary to obtain the pregnant minor's parents' consent to the medical care related to the delivery. Often this issue caused the minors to flee the agency into the black market where legal niceties were not a problem.

After some thought, I drafted a legislative bill that was passed creating Section 34.5 of the civil code. It stated:

§ 34.5   Minors: contracts not disaffirmable; pregnancy care – Notwithstanding any other provision of the law, an unmarried minor may give consent to the furnishing of hospital, medical and surgical care related to the prevention or treatment of pregnancy, and such consent shall not be subject to disaffirmance because of minority. The consent of the parent or parents of such minor shall not be necessary in order to authorize such hospital, medical and surgical care.

The provisions of this section shall not be construed to authorize a minor to be sterilized without the consent of his or her parent or guardian.

Everybody was satisfied until the California Supreme Court in the 1971 case of *Ballard v. Anderson,* 4 C. 3d 873, in a divided court four-to-three decision authored by Justice Stanley Mosk, interpreted Section 34.5 as emancipating a minor for the purpose of obtaining therapeutic abortions without parental consent. This was what I have called an example of the law of unintended consequences.

❦ *The Consent Manual*

Because of the many questions about consents and the fact that our office was continually receiving requests from hospitals to review their consent forms, I became increasingly concerned about the fact that there was no uniform pattern of the forms or procedures being followed. So I requested and received from the board of the Hospital Council of Southern California permission to explore the possibility of developing model forms to be used by all hospitals in Southern California.

The first step was to communicate with the major hospitals in Los Angeles and request copies of all of the consent forms currently in use. About 20 hospitals responded and I sorted out the forms into piles around our dining room table, trying to make some sense out of them. There were consent forms of a simple paragraph, others of several pages, some primarily to protect the hospital, others obviously originated by one of the physician specialty sections and others seemingly designed to punish the patient. The exercise did however identify issues that needed to be covered.

My first decision was that there should be two basic forms— one for hospital admission, the other for the physician surgery consent, even though they should logically be interrelated. Taking the hospital form first, the question became what the document should be conceptually and what should be its title.

On this point I was strongly influenced by my experience with a lawsuit brought against White Memorial Hospital involving a patient who had apparently been very difficult in continuously calling the night-shift nurse. She was overburdened and became exasperated with the calls made by this patient pulling the bedside signal cord which buzzed the nursing station and flashed the light outside the patient's room. The nurse finally strode into the room, pulled out the pair of scissors that all nurses then carried, and proceeded to cut the call cord so the patient could not reach it and went on about her business.

The lawsuit was not an ordinary allegation of malpractice but was for breach of contract for failure to provide proper nursing service. The reason for this legal approach was soon evident. The malpractice statute of limitations had run, so to stay in court the attorney sued for breach of contract for failing to provide satisfactory nursing care for which the statute had not run, relying on the fact that the admission document signed by the patient was entitled "Hospital Agreement" and therefore was a contract to provide a specified service. The lawyer claimed this as the basis for the suit. As a practical matter, I was successful in having the case dismissed on the grounds it was truly barred by the malpractice statute. However, it alerted me to consider the issue when I drew up the model hospital admission document.

To avoid the contract issue I titled the document "Conditions of Admission" and provided that by signing the document the patient or the patient's representative accepted the described conditions under which the hospital proposed to provide care. Since it was not a negotiated contract it did not require a signature by a designated representative of the hospital and thus avoided an element of red tape.

The most radical requirement I made was that the hospital give the patient a copy of the document the patient signed. Prior to this it was not customary for hospitals to give patients copies of the admission documents or other forms signed. There was considerable resistance to this approach until we explained that if the patient did not have a copy there was a good chance the patient could legally avoid the terms by claiming not to have been given an opportunity to read and understand the document signed.

The model form emphasized the role of the patient's physician as distinguished from the role of the hospital. In this regard there was a general consent to medical and surgical procedures to cover those services furnished by the hospital, emphasizing that the hospital would follow the instructions of the attending physician and that it was the responsibility of the patient's attending physician to obtain the patient's informed consent as to surgery or potentially hazardous procedures. This was a controversial issue as many physicians wanted to make the hospital nurses or admitting personnel responsible for obtaining the informed consent.

It was my opinion, fortunately supported by the California Medical Association, that the attending physician was the only person in a position to respond to a patient's questions and give a knowledgeable explanation of the course of treatment, together with the possible complications and alternate treatment possibilities. This approach was not entirely acceptable to many physicians who wanted to argue with me that the hospital nurse should obtain the informed consent.

My response to those physicians was that as far as the patient was concerned, the most risky choice to be made was the selection of the physician, and if the hospitals were to be involved in obtaining a true informed consent, the nurse or admitting individual would be required to explain the risks of utilizing the particular physician and what the physician's record was on outcomes. I then suggested we could post in the admission office a chart of Las Vegas odds on each physician outcomes by procedure. That effectively closed the discussion.

As we now watch current development of outcomes data on hospitals and physicians, my suggestion does not seem so far out. We may find eventually, as a matter of law or regulation, it is mandated that a patient is entitled to current outcome experience of both physicians and hospitals as well as managed-care plans.

The model "Conditions of Admission" form has been only slightly modified since its first publication in 1960. A new paragraph has been added entitled "Healthcare service plan obligations" which is certainly necessary from the point of view of the patient as well as the hospital and the managed-care plans. However, this paragraph deals with the interparty financial relationships and not with the issues of utilization control and the potential liability problems involved in the implementation of managed care.

Equally important to the development of the "Conditions of Admission" was the drafting of a model surgical consent form entitled, "Authorization for and Consent to Surgery or Special Diagnostic or Therapeutic Procedures". This form was created primarily to protect the hospital although certain basic information and instructions were included to cover such special procedures as laboratory tests, x-rays and instructions related to disposition of organs or other tissue removal from the patient. Again, a primary purpose was to encourage the patient to communicate with the attending physician or surgeon for information as to the nature of the procedure to be performed, the nature of the risks and the possibility of alternative approaches.

During this process of designing a set of model consents I received a copy of a procedures manual published by the Kaiser Permanente hospitals. It appeared to be extremely useful for these hospitals so I proposed developing a model manual for all hospitals. This project was approved and led to the design and drafting of what I called "The Consent Manual" because initially it dealt with the basic consent forms to be used in all California hospitals.

It was our hope that by establishing a uniform community

practice, any physician or hospital following this procedure would be protected from litigation. Actually, my original intent was that the model manual be available for each hospital to use as a basis for designing its own manual. However, over the years it has become a separate free-standing tool for use of all hospital personnel, also serving as an educational tool since the written material included an explanation of the purpose of each form and the legal consequences of not following the recommended procedures. In drafting these forms my colleagues and I have tried to be user-friendly, emphasizing information in lay language with the minimum use of technical terms.

— regulation is ongoing nothing NEW

With the rapidly increasing regulation of healthcare, I discussed with the CHA board whether the Consent Manual should be expanded to cover these matters or whether a separate manual should be published. The decision was made to include all such health matters in the Consent Manual, much of this having little to do with the subject of consents. This required the entire Manual be reviewed after each session of the Legislature to incorporate legislative changes, as well as pertinent actions by administrative agencies in the health field together with pertinent court decisions.

The 22nd edition was published in 1996 as the standard-setting publication for the industry for 36 years since its first publication in 1960. It now is 840 pages in length. With the permission of CHA the manual format has been copied and adopted by many state hospital associations for their own constituencies.

❦ Informed Consents

Just about the time we thought we had the problem of consents under control in the early 1970s, physicians and hospitals were hit with a new rash of litigation, now described as the liability for lack of an informed consent. This was a major expansion of court-created law on the rights of patients to know and to participate in decisions relating to treatment. There was a wide variety of requirements made by various state and federal courts. As examples of this new right for the patient to know were such issues as:

- Existence of alternative treatments.
- The likely result of the proposed procedures, including possible death.
- Possible side effects, including the approximate percentage of risk.

Various standards were set by the courts. One was the professional duty of the medical community for disclosure by a medical standard. The alternative test was an individual standard as to whether the patients in question would have consented to the particular treatment if they had known the risk of the alternatives. The right of the patient not to know and to rely on the judgment of the physician was also recognized.

This soon became a national issue and the medical community demanded legislative action, not only to clarify the law and the nature of physician liability but also to include safe-harbor provisions specifically setting forth the written form of disclosure and consent that would act as an absolute protection to the physician against liability for failure to obtain an informed consent.

California courts were leaders in creating new liability concepts and disclosure requirements. Jointly with the California Medical Association (CMA) we were deeply concerned about this development, and on behalf of the CHA we had extensive discussions with Mr. Hassard and Mr. Willett, counsel for CMA, on developing a resolution. Although we had followed a legislative approach to solve earlier consent issues, after reviewing the actions taken in other states we were horrified at the complexity and rigidity of the various state legislative actions. As a result we jointly proposed a voluntary solution.

Under this approach, counsel for CHA and CMA convened a series of panels from the various medical specialty societies to develop individual protocols for each specialty. Using this approach we had each group develop its own indicated protocol under which it outlined the major risk procedures of their specialty, alternative treatments and the risks involved. We thus avoided the "one form fits all" and made the approach much more patient-friendly and understandable. Each specialty society with the coöperation of the individual medical staffs took responsibility for the indoctrination of its constituents.

Based on recent personal experiences in consulting with physicians, I have been uniformly impressed with how they have dealt with the informed consent. Rather than resorting to legislation we relied on what can best be described as the practice of good medicine in the best interest of good patient care by encouraging better physician-patient communication.

The ultimate creation by the American Hospital Association of a Patient Bill of Rights is part of the improvement of communication with patients. Of current interest is the movement at both the state and national levels to create a special patient bill of rights to improve and clarify the relationship of the patient to the evolving managed-care system. It will be interesting to see whether the managed-care industry can develop and sell to the public a voluntary approach or if this time it requires a legislated answer.

In spite of the efforts of both organized medicine and hospitals, litigation over the existence of an informed consent continues to be reported as one of the most frequently litigated types of alleged medical malpractice.

5

Welfare Property Tax Exemption

Prior to World War II California property tax law did not provide for the exemption of religious and charitable organizations, although most states granted such an exemption.

When I started to practice in 1940 one of my assignments was to obtain a reduction of the property taxes for certain of our client hospitals. The procedure followed was for each hospital, on receipt of its city and county tax bills, to file a petition to the board of supervisors for a reduction in the assessed value of the institution.

The Los Angeles County Board of Supervisors would set a hearing date for all the petitions and a group of us would appear to go through an established process. Basically, each one representing a hospital would argue that the hospital building had been grossly over-assessed because it was a structure that was essentially for a single purpose with little commercial value. If indicated, we would point out that the configuration of the entrances with their broad staircases as well as their interiors further reduced their value. The Board of Supervisors would solemnly listen to this ritual and then go into executive session after which it was reported that the assessed value of all of the applicant hospitals was reduced 50 percent.

I participated in this process for two years prior to going into the navy. However, in my second year there was a dramatic turn of events. In the midst of the hearing one of the hospital representatives collapsed during his presentation, was laid out on the table between the board members and the rest of us, and was ultimately declared dead. Needless to say, the supervisors adjourned the proceedings. In the aftermath the hospital representatives got together to develop a better procedure. The result was an agreement to take the necessary legislative and constitutional steps to obtain a total exemption for the future.

The legal problem confronted was that to obtain an exemption it would be necessary to amend the California Constitution. Thus the California Hospital Association appealed to the 1943 session of the Legislature to adopt proposed Constitutional Amendment #13 by a two-thirds majority of both houses, to be placed on the November 7, 1944, ballot as Proposition Number 4. This was approved by the voters and Article 1c. entitled "Exemptions: Property for Religious, Hospital or Charitable Purposes" provided:

> Sec. 1c. In addition to such exemptions as are now provided in this Constitution, the Legislature may exempt from taxation all or any portion of property used exclusively for religious, hospital or charitable purposes and owned by community chests, funds, foundations or corporations organized and operated for religious, hospital or charitable purposes, not conducted for profit and no part of the net earnings of which inures to the benefit of any private shareholder or individual.

Rather than a direct constitutional grant of exemption, the language provided a broad delegation of power to the Legislature to design and implement the exemption language itself following the classic not-for-profit approach. There was one important exception: we included the word "hospital" in the definition of exempt purposes based on our experience with the lack of such word in the language of the unemployment insurance tax exemption discussed above. However, as helpful as the word was, we were to find out in litigation that followed, there was now a need to define the "word" hospital, a process that has continued up through the 1992 *Rideout Hospital Foundation, Inc. v. County of Yuba,* 10 Cal. Rptr. 2d 141.

The 1945 Legislature exercised its new authority to grant property tax exemptions to various charitable purposes, including hospitals. The language specifically applicable to hospitals was:

> Property used exclusively for religious, hospital, scientific, or charitable purposes owned and operated by community chests, funds, foundations or corporations organized and operated for religious, hospital, scientific, or charitable purposes is exempt from taxation if:
>
> (1) The owner is not organized or operated for profit;
>
> (2) No part of the net earnings of the owner inures to the benefit of any private shareholder or individual;
>
> (3) The property is not used or operated by the owner or by any other person for profit regardless of the purposes to which the profit is devoted;
>
> (4) The property is not used or operated by the owner or by any other person so as to benefit any officer, trustee, director, shareholder, member, employee, contributor, or bondholder of the owner or operator, or any other person, through the distribution of profits, payment of excessive charges or compensations or the more advantageous pursuit of their business or profession;
>
> (5) The property is not used by the owner or members thereof for fraternal or lodge purposes, or for social club purposes except where such use is clearly incidental to a primary religious, hospital, scientific, or charitable purpose;
>
> (6) The property is irrevocably dedicated to religious, charitable, scientific, or hospital purposes and upon the liquidation, dissolution or abandonment of the owner will not inure to the benefit of any private person except a fund, foundation or corporation organized and operated for religious, hospital, scientific, for charitable purposes.

The exemption provided for herein shall be known as the "welfare exemption." This exemption shall be in addition to any other exemption now provided by law. This section shall not be construed an exemption to property held by or used as an educational institution of less than collegiate grade.

Implementation of the above language was placed in the jurisdiction of the individual county assessors, but the law provided that the required exemption affidavit of each individual hospital be reviewed by the State Board of Equalization, which in turn made a recommendation to each assessor on whether or not the particular property complied with the exemption language. However, individual assessors took unilateral action to deny the exemption in certain situations; that led to a continued flow of litigation. It became my duty, on behalf of the California Hospital Association, to monitor the activities of the assessors and advise the hospitals whether or not to initiate litigation to challenge a denial.

The State Board of Equalization and the various local tax assessors put us to the test as they continued to attempt to whittle down the parameters of the tax exemption. As a result we were kept busy putting out bonfires.

The first litigation was triggered by the Los Angeles County Assessor, who was particularly aggressive in denying the exemption to such items as housing for essential hospital employees, buildings under construction, a tennis court maintained for recreation facilities for hospital employees, including interns and student nurses, and a "thrift shop" operated for the sale of donated clothing to support a free children's clinic.

We combined the exemption denials for three leading non-profit hospitals with religious sponsorship into one legal action against the County of Los Angeles to challenge this action. These included Cedars of Lebanon Hospital, Hollywood Presbyterian Hospital and the California Hospital, owned and operated by the Lutheran Hospital Society. In a landmark decision in August of 1950 the California Supreme Court in *Cedars of Lebanon Hospital v. County of Los Angeles* upheld the exemption as to property used for a nurses' training school and housing for hospital interns, resident doctors and other essential employees and the tennis court as a recreation facility, but denied it as to buildings under construction as not then being "used" exclusively for exempt purposes. The same result applied to the thrift shop as not being reasonably necessary for accomplishment of hospital purposes.

The most important part of this decision was the court's acceptance of the definition of a hospital which we proposed in our briefs as follows:

> In determining what constitutes "property used exclusively for ... hospital ... purposes," it is appropriate first to note generally the nature of a "hospital." A fair and unchallenged description of the nature of such an institution is set forth in plaintiffs' combined brief as follows: "A hospital is primarily a service organization. It serves three groups: the patients, its doctors, and the public. It furnishes a place where the patient, whether poor or rich, can be treated under ideal conditions. It makes available room, special diet, X-ray, laboratory, surgery, and a multitude of other services and equipment now available through the advances of medical science. Essential to the administration of these techniques is the corps of highly-trained nurses and student nurses who are on duty 24 hours per day. In the large hospitals there are the interns and residents whose presence makes it possible for the hospital to do a better job. In addition, the hospital ... must have administration to see that its services function properly and are coordinated, and that patients are received and cared for regardless of the hour or the patient's condition. Nothing can be left to chance because a slip may mean a life or many lives. These facilities also stand ready to serve the community in times of epidemic or disaster."
>
> This description expresses in general terms the nature, functions, and purposes of a complete, modern hospital plant, which functions and purposes are more fully and more specifically alleged in the complaints on file herein and are admitted by the demurrers thereto. And as the constitutional amendment and statute under consideration were adopted and enacted in 1944 and 1945, respectively, it is entirely clear that the people and the Legislature had in mind such a complete, modern hospital plant

rather than one consisting only of the minimum and indispens-
able facilities found in earlier hospitals which inadequately
served their purposes many years ago.

There then followed two cases involving an interpretation of
the language in Section 214 of the Revenue Code which established
the condition on the exemption that "the property is not used or
operated by the owner or by any other person for profit regardless
of the purpose to which the profit is devoted."

The first case involved the Sutter Hospital in Sacramento. The
hospital had assets of $705,000 and a bonded indebtedness of
$272,000. For the year 1945 the surplus of income over current
expenses, which included interest payments and depreciation, came
to $87,000 and in 1946 this amounted to $107,000, or a surplus
each year slightly in excess of eight percent of gross income. The
surplus was used for debt retirement and expansion of facilities.
The hospital conceded it intended to make an operating profit for
these purposes. The Supreme Court held that the issue was not
whether there was a "profit" but whether there was intent to make
a profit and, based on the facts, affirmed the lower court decision
to deny the total hospital exemption.

The second case, decided in 1955, involved St. Francis Hospital
in San Francisco. The factual issue arose because the hospital had
an operating surplus of $130,000 from operating a medical office
building which included not only offices rented to doctors and
dentists but also a pharmacy and coffee shop and a parking lot
used by patients of both the doctors and the hospital. The building
was not exempt, but the question was whether the receipt of net
income from the building would forfeit the exemption for the
hospital. The appellate court held that these income-producing
activities in the context of the total hospital operation was not
grounds for denying the exemption to the main hospital structure.

The distinction between the two cases is that the St. Francis
issue dealt with profit from buildings for which no exemption

could be claimed, whereas the Sutter case concerned profit being developed from the principal hospital structure. However, after the decision in the Sutter case there was concern as to its application to the principal hospital buildings.

During the spring of 1953 I received a telephone call from Gene Salisbury, who was then the full-time president of the California Hospital Association as well as its chief lobbyist. He called from a telephone booth outside of a hearing room in the state capitol building to report that the Revenue and Taxation Committee of the Assembly was considering a bill to amend the welfare exemption and that the chief administrative officer of Sacramento County had gotten the committee's ear on the need to limit the threshold on the amount of profit permitted by hospitals who were enjoying the welfare exemption and that the Legislature should define profit to limit abuses by hospitals.

Gene wanted some language immediately that would not adversely affect our hospital constituency. I had given this some thought following the Sutter Hospital case and dictated the following language to be inserted in the welfare exemption:

> The owner is not organized or operated for profit; provided, that in the case of hospitals, such organization shall not be deemed to be organized or operated for profit, if during the immediate preceding fiscal year the excess of operating revenues, exclusive of gifts, endowments and grants-in-aid, over operating expenses shall not have exceeded a sum equivalent to ten percent of such operating expenses. As used herein, operating expenses shall include depreciation based on cost of replacement and amortization of, and interest on, indebtedness ...

Gene succeeded in getting the language into the bill and it was adopted. Ever since, the accountants have shaken their heads as to my definition of "profit" because it would take an extraordinary circumstance for a not-for-profit hospital to earn a profit in excess of that definition. The net result was that this amendment strengthened the exemption for hospitals rather than limited it, as was established in the *Rideout Hospital Foundation, Inc.* case discussed later here.

Of historical importance in the art of legislative negotiations is that in drafting the 1953 amendment bill, as adopted, several sections included, in addition to the above revision of subparagraph (1) of Section 214 of the Revenue and Taxation Code, additional measures designed to accomplish two purposes. The first was to insert an urgency clause which, while requiring a two-thirds affirmative vote of each house to pass, would make the bill effective on the governor's signature rather than delaying to the next January 1st so that the terms of the amendment to Section 214 would be in effect for the year 1953. The second additional provision set forth the reason for the legislation as well as its purpose. Such additional language could have a very important impact on future decisions of the court on matters rising out of the legislation.

Some of my most frustrating experiences had been in arguing the application of a specific piece of legislation before a court, either trial or appellate, and having the judge or justice opine upon what he or she thinks the Legislature intended, when I knew darn well as a drafter of the bill what was intended, for I had done it. If legislative intent is not expressed in the bill, then the court may create its own belief as to the intent of the Legislature which may be at substantial variance to the intention of the original authors of the legislation.

We learned from our experience with the welfare exemption cases the importance of this technique. Later, in developing the Medical Injury Compensation Reform Act of 1975, the statements of intent that we placed in the bill had a major impact upon its eventual interpretation as well as its constitutionality. Interestingly enough, while writing this chapter I was serving on the drafting committee of the coalition created to fight for national malpractice tort reform. One of the most important contributions made to that work by the California representatives to the coalition was the introduction of both findings of fact as well as statements of Congressional intent for the benefit of all states.

In the 1992 case of *Rideout Hospital Foundation, Inc. v. County of Yuba,* 10 Cal. Rptr. 2d 141, the district court of appeal was faced with the question whether under the amended language of Section 214, a hospital which earned more than the ten percent figure was automatically disqualified from enjoying the tax exemption. The court, relying heavily on the statement of intent together with a history of the problem sought to be solved by the amendment, ruled that the ten percent limit was really a safe harbor and that a hospital which earned in excess of the ten percent could still qualify for the exemption if the hospital can show that it was not organized or operated for profit.

The court relied upon our legislative intent statement in the urgency clause that it has never been the Legislature's intent "that the property of ... hospital ... organizations otherwise qualifying for the welfare exemption should be denied exemption if the income from the actual operation of the property for the exempt activities be devoted to the purpose of debt retirement, expansion of plant and facilities or reserve for operating contingencies...."

In fact, back in 1953 when the amendment was added, emphasis was made on the need for hospitals to have an operating surplus so they could expand. Expansion is no longer a high priority.

Ever resourceful tax assessors then raised yet another problem: Were hospital buildings under construction "used exclusively for charitable purposes"? We determined that the best way to solve this issue was to obtain appropriate legislation. As a result, Section 214.1 of the Revenue and Taxation Code was introduced and adopted which defined as exempt "facilities in the course of construction after the 1st Monday of March 1954 together with the land on which the facilities are located as may be required for their convenient use and occupancy." This legislation required a constitutional amendment before it was effective and this was achieved at the November 1954 general election.

However, this was not enough as the tax assessors then refused to exempt buildings which were razed, so that Section 214.2 was adopted in 1959 defining buildings under construction to include buildings being demolished or razed if there was an intent to replace them with facilities to be used exclusively for religious, charitable or hospital purposes. In its legislative enactment it was recited that "the amendments made by this act do not constitute a change in, but are declaratory of the pre-existing law"; thus the law became retroactive in its effect.

Another problem developed in 1954 in Santa Barbara County when the assessor denied an exemption to the space used by the radiologist as well as the radiology equipment at Cottage Hospital. Rather than fighting it in the court, the California Hospital Association in 1955 introduced legislation to resolve the problem with a new Section 214.7 to the Revenue and Taxation Code providing:

> In the case of a hospital, neither the use of hospital property nor the receipt of fees or other lawful compensation by a licensed physician for the practice of his profession therein, shall be grounds for denial of the exemption provided by Sections 214 and 254.5. This section does not apply to such portion of the hospital as may be leased or rented to a physician for his office for the general practice of medicine.

The bill was made retroactive by its terms to January 1, 1955.

One of the unanticipated consequences of the adoption of the welfare exemption amendment in the California Constitution was that it led to the property tax exemption of nonprofit private schools of less than collegiate grade, the legality and constitutionality of which was then established by the California courts and ultimately approved by the U.S. Supreme Court. The Legislature adopted amendments to Section 214 of the Revenue and Taxation Code in 1951 exempting such schools and the California Supreme Court, in *Lundberg v. County of Alameda*, 46 C.2d 644 (June 1956), upheld the constitutionality of the statute under the definition of "charitable purpose." I participated in the strategy for obtaining legislative action and appeared as amicus in support of the schools in the above case. Because the exemption covered Catholic parochial schools it was a hot issue at the time.

6

Early Patient Healthcare Issues

❦ Blood Problems

From a health policy point of view there are at least three critical issues faced by hospitals and physicians directly related to the use of blood.

The first and on-going issue is the fact that to some constituent groups, such as the Jehovah's Witnesses, blood has significant religious connotations, so they must refuse the utilization of human blood as a component of medical care. Over the years this conflict with generally accepted medical practice has been resolved by practical solutions including the availability of physicians and surgeons who specialize in what is described as bloodless treatment. There can also be a resort to the courts as described later in this chapter.

Second, in 1955 hospitals and physicians became concerned when in medical malpractice cases involving the use of incompatible blood, plaintiff's attorneys increasingly asserted that under the Uniform Commercial Code the administration of blood or blood products constituted a sale of a product; therefore, under the strict liability concepts of the commercial code, the healthcare provider could be held to have warranted that the product was fit for human use regardless of whether or not a defect in the blood was known or had been created by negligence. In those days the issue was not only the problems of typing and matching the blood but also the initial inability to screen donated blood sufficiently for such contagions as hepatitis and later HIV and other factors as they were discovered.

The third problem was a matter of additional cost. If blood was a product it could be subject to the state sales tax, thus adding an additional patient cost, further complicated by the fact that most blood administered in the hospitals was donated and the charges for it covered the cost of administering, processing and storing the product.

In collaboration with the California Medical Association we presented to the California Legislature at its 1955 session a proposed Section 1623 to the Business and Professions Code which was passed by both houses and signed by the governor. The section provides:

Business and Professions Code Section 1623.
The procurement, processing, distribution, or the use of whole blood, plasma, blood products, and blood derivatives for the purpose of injecting or transfusing the same, or any of them into the human body shall be construed to be, and is declared to be, for all purposes whatsoever, the rendition of a service by each and every person, firm, or corporation participating therein, and shall not be construed to be, and is declared not to be, a sale of such whole blood, plasma, blood products or blood derivatives, for any purpose or purposes whatsoever.

This action did not eliminate possible liability for negligent processing or administering of blood but it did secure a balance between the critical need for this medical resource and the protection of the patient. Hopefully, in the long run present research will develop an artificial substitute for human blood that will eliminate major risks and also be cost effective. Also, by classifying blood as a service rather than a product we eliminated the application of the sales tax, thus solving that problem.

❦ Burns, Explosions and Cardiac Arrest

Whenever we had the feeling we were at last getting a handle on stabilizing the spread of malpractice claims, there would be dramatic progress in the technology or the practice of medicine that would create new potentials for liability.

Two manifestations in this trend involved surgery. The problems began to manifest themselves about 1960 with an increased frequency of patients suffering from burns during surgery, as well as from occasional fires or explosions during anesthesia. Fortunately, both of these matters were subject to solution but each required substantial time and research.

As far as the burns, the problem arose from the rapid expansion in the use of electric cautery instruments to stop bleeding in the surgical field. It was discovered that clothing worn by the surgeons and technicians could accumulate static electricity which in turn could be conducted to the patient so that a spark from the cautery or another electric source could cause a surge of electricity that would burn the patient. The problem was aggravated by the fact that many of the floors in the surgical suite were not conductive and therefore could not drain off the static electricity. A substantial modification of the surgery floors plus careful care in their treatment and maintenance was essential to avoid the occurrence.

A related problem came from the selection and control of the anesthetic gases. It was found that certain mixtures of gases could become flammable or explosive when triggered by the cautery or static electricity. Because of preventive work, the number of claims per thousand of burn cases was reduced from approximately two per thousand occupied beds per year in 1963 to less than half of that number by 1973.

The next problem area, and one far more serious than burns, was that of cardiac arrest. This involved factors both from within and without the hospital walls. Beginning in 1960 and rapidly increasing thereafter there was much media attention given to dramatic action taken on the street or in public areas in which an individual suffering from a cardiac arrest was saved by the prompt action of some spectator who applied closed-chest cardiac resuscitation under extraordinary circumstances.

This produced a great increase in the awareness of the public regarding the possibility of reversing a cardiac arrest. The logical question raised in the media was why cardiac resuscitation wasn't always successfully done in the hospital when amateurs on the street could even do it? Of course, there was little media probing or publicity about the cases in which cardiac arrest treatment was only partially successful with the disastrous results of severe permanent brain damages.

Initially this was only a matter of closed chest resuscitation, a technique that had been used in partial drowning cases in the past. However, the actions in public took a new turn as non-doctors would attempt open chest resuscitation by opening the chest with a penknife or other available instrument – with occasional dramatic successful outcomes. The challenge was for hospitals and their personnel to achieve completely satisfactory conclusions for in-house occurrences. The juries had little sympathy for a hospital or physician's failure to achieve a 100 percent satisfactory success and they granted boxcar judgments for failure.

The hospital response to this was cardiopulmonary resuscitation (C.P.R.) training for all personnel, the use of better designed and equipped "crash carts" to respond to a code blue (the emergency call for a cardiac arrest team in the hospital), and the development of treatment protocols to deal with specific situations in both the patient room and the surgery suite.

From a liability point of view the hospital was faced with a Hobson's choice – if their staff attempted to save the patient's life and only partially succeeded, the legal damages would be greater than if the patient had died. This raised the issue of how long there should be extraordinary efforts made to save the patient. Stanford University Hospital conducted an early research project to determine how long the effort should be made and then installed a clock in each surgery so if a cardiac arrest occurred in surgery, the surgery personnel could call out the seconds as they passed until the established limit for the effort was reached.

The number of claims per thousand occupied beds for cardiac arrest multiplied by ten between years 1960 and 1972, with the bulk of the increase occurring between 1970 and 1972. After this there was a major drop beginning in 1973 and thereafter as hospitals became better organized to prevent these occurrences.

One serious problem that arose out of this development was the matter of handling "do not resuscitate" requests by patients. As the patient population became more knowledgeable about the consequences of a cardiac arrest and the attempts to resuscitate, many patients preferred not to take the risk of a bad result or for other reasons were ready to die with dignity. Patients began asking their attending physicians not to resuscitate them with what was called a "D.N.R." order or a "No Code" order.

Initially the doctors were sympathetic to the patient's desires, but then they were faced with the problem of how to communicate with the patient's family in the event a No Code was called and the patient expired. A variety of subterfuges were developed, the most frequent being a colored paper clip attached to the patient's chart to indicate to the nursing staff not to issue a code blue in the event of a cardiac arrest.

This pattern had gone on for quite a while when a hospital

asked our legal opinion about the practice. We were sympathetic about the hospital's desire to comply with the patient's wishes, but we also were very concerned about the ultimate legal responsibility for the hospital and its nursing personnel in the event there was litigation over the authority of the hospital and nursing staff to fail to initiate immediate cardiac resuscitation. We therefore concluded that a "do not resuscitate" order must be entered into the chart by the attending physician with no informal alternatives. This direction was not appreciated by a number of physicians but ultimately they recognized the importance of not only communicating with the patient but with the patient's family over this critical issue.

Now with the public and legal concern over physician assisted suicide, the issue will again be highlighted in the courts even though the U.S. Supreme Court has recognized the legal right of a patient to refuse care such as resuscitation.

❦ Life or Death

Historically, it has always been an important role of our office to assist hospitals and their component parts in reaching critical decisions concerning patient care. Although it is not our place to make the final decision, we often have been of assistance in working out a process for that final decision making.

Problems relating to the declaration of death in a hospital or a long-term care facility were frequent and aggravating to both physicians and hospital personnel, particularly when the death occurred at night and it was necessary to call the attending physician in to make the declaration. As attorneys for the hospitals we had taken the position that only the patient's attending physician could make this declaration. Also, there was no clear statement as to the clinical basis for making the declaration. After discussing this with Mr. Hassard and Mr. Willett in their capacity of legal counsel to the CMA, it was determined we should jointly support legislation on this subject and, at the same time, endeavor to resolve the additional issue of the legal and ethical roles of physicians in situations involving a potential organ transplant which were then becoming medically feasible.

There were a few statutes and voluntary protocols existing in other states, particularly one known as the Harvard protocol, which we studied; we concluded all of them were unnecessarily complicated. Consequently we jointly drafted and proposed adding Sections 7180-7182 to the Health and Safety Code. These measures substantially solved the problem by requiring that physicians could make the declaration of death when they had determined that the patient had suffered a total and irreversible cessation of brain function and this fact had been independently confirmed by another physician. At the same time the legislation prohibited either of those physicians from participating in future procedures for removing or transplanting an organ of the deceased patient.

At a recent conference at USC School of Medicine, the leading USC transplant surgeon stated that there had been a dramatic progress in the use of transplants in California due to the clarity and simplicity of the California statute on declaration of death.

I did not bring to his attention an incident in which I had recently participated. The CMA had asked me to conduct a meeting with California Assemblyperson Richard Katz and some of his constituents who were proposing an amendment to the declaration of death statute requiring that, in addition to a finding of brain death, there also must be a finding of the complete cessation of the ability to maintain the function of the heart. Their concern was based on a religious belief that the human soul was centered in the heart and not the brain and that our statute, being mandatory, interfered with their adherents' religious concepts of continued life when it was still possible to maintain the function of the heart with the use of a heart pump, a relatively common procedure which could continue for an extended number of days beyond the finding of brain death.

The religious group constituency was probably some 20,000 individuals located in one general area of West Los Angeles. After a long philosophical discussion as well as our pointing out potential statewide economic impact of such an amendment they finally agreed to withdraw their proposed statute if we would share their concerns with the hospitals and physicians in their home vicinity — which we did.

This is just another example of the potential unintended consequences of solving a medical problem by statute. I am sure we could have defeated the proposal in the Legislature, but there would have been bad feeling and obviously these individuals had the right to have their ethical views seriously considered.

The 1974 statutes, which have never been amended, are set forth as follows:

§ 7180. Pronouncement on determining cessation of brain function: Confirmation: Other procedures

A person shall be pronounced dead if it is determined by a physician that the person has suffered a total and irreversible cessation of brain function. There shall be independent confirmation of the death by another physician.

Nothing in this chapter shall prohibit a physician from using other usual and customary procedures for determining death as the exclusive basis for pronouncing a person dead.

§ 7181. Confirmation in event of transplantation under Uniform Anatomical Gift Act: Restriction on physicians' participation in removal and transplantation.

When a part of the donor is used for direct transplantation pursuant to the Uniform Anatomical Gift Act (Chapter 3.5 [commencing with Section 7150]) and the death of the donor is determined by determining that the person has suffered a total and irreversible cessation of brain function, there shall be an independent confirmation of the death by another physician. Neither the physician making the determination of death under Section 7155.5 nor the physician making the independent confirmation shall participate in the procedures for removing or transplanting a part.

§ 7182. Patient medical records

Complete patient medical records required of a health facility pursuant to regulations adopted by the department in accordance with Section 1275 shall be kept, maintained, and preserved with respect to the requirements of this chapter when a person is pronounced dead by determining that the person has suffered a total and irreversible cessation of brain function.

A sensitive legal question relative to the availability of life-support medical resources came to me in a telephone request from Childrens Hospital of Los Angeles some 30 years ago. It arose out of a federal program to provide a limited number of heart- and lung-support machines to a select group of children hospitals for the purpose of providing short-term life support to children being scheduled for kidney transplants. The machines were not to be used for long-term care.

What had happened at Childrens was that a family that adhered to the Jehovah's Witness faith had a ten-year old son with a serious nephrology problem, but the family refused to consider a kidney transplant because of the potential need for a blood transfusion. Therefore the patient was not eligible for the federal heart/lung machine program. However, the family brought the child to the Childrens emergency department after midnight where the resident in charge put the child on one of the machines.

It was the opinion of surgeons that legal steps should be taken to override the parents' refusal to consent to the transplant. My advice was that we should refer this matter to the juvenile court, and it was arranged to have a court hearing at the hospital. As part of the preparation for the hearing, I asked for a clinical conference at the hospital to include the attending physician, the surgeons, the nurses, the social workers and any others who might be involved in the decision to pursue surgical intervention against the parents' wishes and who might also be potential witnesses at the hearing.

We had about 15 people assembled around the board room table for the process. Each one there gave their viewpoint and justification for action, which was substantially unanimous in favor of requesting authority from the court to go ahead. The last person I called on was a psychiatrist who then gave us an unanticipated evaluation of the status of the child. The psychiatrist was of the opinion that the child fully understood the issues involved and, more importantly, was fully committed to the religious viewpoint of his parents. If the surgery proceeded under a court order it was the psychiatrist's conclusion that the child would refuse to coöperate in his care and the prognosis of recovery would be very doubtful.

Needless to say, this viewpoint had a major impact on the group and as I then quizzed each one as to their opinion there was an almost complete reversal resulting in a group decision not to recommend action. I immediately contacted the attorney for the family and he agreed to seek a physician committed to treating Jehovah's Witness patients and arrange for a discharge to his care, which he did. I have often wondered what happened to that child as he never returned to Childrens Hospital.

This, however, is an excellent example of what happens every day in the hospital setting as healthcare providers struggle with the issues of priorities and rationing of limited healthcare resources.

7

Hospital Personnel Problems

The relationship between hospitals and their employees has always been a matter of personal concern to me. Before continuing, I should state I firmly believe that hospitals in the best interest of patient care must recruit, train and motivate their personnel in a thoroughly responsible manner. The quality of care that patients receive is a direct result of management's commitment to that end. Further, hospitals are organizationally so complex through the need for specialization and a broad spectrum of mandatory personal licensure of their various professions and technicians, that the potential for internal conflict and failure to exercise needed flexibility is always a threat.

My concern has been that hospitals might follow the pattern of railroads – which also have numerous specific licensed personnel groups. The unionization of these specialized groups created a multiplicity of little fiefdoms which forever enfeebled the railroads. Thus I came to the conclusion that the move for unionization of hospital personnel was not in the best interest of patient care, if hospital administration properly performs its role of accountability to its employees. In other words, unionization is generally the price paid for management failure in how it handles and compensates its employees. Equally important is my position that hospitals in their employment practices are not in the welfare business. It is vital that they employ qualified personnel and not scrape the bottom of the barrel by recruiting from the minimum-wage group.

In this regard I have long been concerned that California hospitals not repeat the mistake made by the New York hospitals of using less qualified employees for their service component of the hospital and paying the minimum wage. That mistake led to the union organization of these hospitals. A further influence upon my attitude was my experience at the state level with the results of the war labor arbitrations of hospital employee grievances that led to the union organization of the San Francisco Bay hospitals during and after World War II.

As consequence of these arbitrations two competing groups of hospitals were created, one made up primarily of San Francisco hospitals, the other of East Bay hospitals. These two groups operated in a bitter schism that continued for years, adversely affecting their ability to work together on other hospital issues. The unions profited from the competition that grew between the two entities. This mutual antagonism was not only about economic issues but often became bitter on a personal basis. In working with John Brewer and Steve Gamble at the Hospital Council of Southern California we did not want to see a repeat of the problems in the north.

Thus in 1960 I encouraged the Hospital Council to create a personnel practices committee made up of a select group of hospital executives with myself as chair. One sorry note is that there were no personnel directors on the committee for the simple reason that few hospitals had such at that time. In most hospitals personnel matters were the responsibility of the hospital administrators or superintendents, as they were still titled in some places.

The committee, a hard-working group, not only authorized a wage and salary survey but, more importantly, developed a document entitled "The Guideposts for Hospital Personnel Practices," that included many recommendations which at the time were considered quite radical. It began with a model statement of policy to be adopted by the hospital board of trustees:

> Example: "Employees are to be selected fairly, on a basis of their abilities as these correspond to labor needs; that they be appropriately trained for the work to be done; that they receive reasonable wage and non-wage compensation; be assured of promotion on the basis of ability and performance; be assured of a fair hearing for their grievances; be guaranteed that no discrimination among them will be made on the basis of race or creed; be assured that management will seek to anticipate the need for adjustments instead of waiting for dissatisfaction to develop; be promised working conditions as safe as is reasonably possible; and be assured that management will always consider the dignity and basic human needs of its employees."

It then recommended the designation of a central authority within the hospital as a "personnel department" with its own director, detailing specific essential components of a personnel program which included the following:

1. Written job descriptions.
2. Development of work standards and periodic review of individual performances.
3. Position control with an adequate personnel budget and appropriate record keeping.
4. Careful selection and placement of employees, including pre-employment and annual physicals at hospital expense.
5. A fair and just wage program which is carefully and honestly administered.
6. A schedule of recommended basic non-wage benefits, plus a list of optional benefits, such as life insurance, retirement benefits, disability insurance and employee discounts, if all employees are treated alike.

7. A grievance procedure included in the personnel manual.
8. Supervisorial training.
9. Good communications – two ways.
10. Safety committee.
11. Personnel advisory committee made up of employees to assist in making recommendations and implementing the other elements of the program.
12. Statement of personnel policies with a separate manual for supervisors.
13. A personnel audit.

The committee next drafted a statement on a "Code of Ethics on Recruitment Practices For Hospitals," because of periodic shortages of certain classes of hospital employees, such as nurses for night shifts, pharmacists and other licensed categories. It was determined that these shortages were not due to an inadequate salary being paid, but primarily due to the lack of educational facilities and teachers, as well as the difficulties of recruiting for night shifts and weekends. By its statement the committee was advising hospitals on how to share the shortage rather than engage in predatory recruitment practices through special bonus plans and the like. This came at a time when there was a movement within hospitals to expand the job assignments for RNs, cutting back on the use of other licensed categories of hospital employees.

The committee recommended that hospitals establish and follow firm recruitment and practice that would avoid:

1. Active seeking out, or attempting to hire away of personnel presently employed in other hospitals in the employment area.
2. Offering such employees voluntarily seeking a change in employment an appointment salary substantially in excess of that one currently being received.
3. Offering a salary, or more rapid salary advancement, or other incentives in excess of the known competitive recruitment level for the area if such incentives are unfairly designed to induce a change in employment.
4. Using job titles or classifications which are not entirely definitive of the position which is being filled in order

to offer a higher salary for the same qualifications which in the general employment area command a lesser salary.

These steps did not resolve the issues within the industry. So as chairperson of the personnel practices committee, I discussed the overall problem with the local head of Griffenhagen and Kroeger (G-K), advisor to the United Way and its members on wage and salary matters. We developed a wholly novel concept, which required the Hospital Council to engage in a professionally staffed, comprehensive wage and salary study of the Southern California hospitals. Based on this study a well-defined job description of each classification would be prepared with a wage differential established for each class, and then the council could present to its members recommendations and findings as to what would be fair compensation for each class for the following year. The compensation should be fair in the marketplace as well as between classes. Regional differences between council districts could be considered.

This survey was targeted at the hospitals that underpaid their workers as well as those that overpaid, although the data did not identify individual hospitals. After reporting to the council board and the participating hospitals, the findings would be made public. This was absolutely unique in a business area where maximum secrecy was the norm and was a complete reversal of the existing practice of keeping such information confidential. Not only would hospital management have access to this critical information, so would hospital employees, unions and the public. More importantly, the information would be available to hospital trustees who ultimately had responsibility for making wage and salary policy decisions for the individual hospital.

It is estimated that at least 60 percent of a hospital's cost is for personnel and this study helped create industry peer pressure to do right by the hospital employees. Also, it would substantially answer the charge by some as to the claimed unfairness of wage differentials. My experience had been that more employees were concerned about what some other job classification received than with the level of their own compensation. Until this survey there was real merit to why employee groups felt wage differentials in hospitals were not rational or fair. Further, this pattern was aggravated by individual hospitals conducting their own telephonic wage surveys which were not accurate or defensible.

In addition to the existing wage information, the report made projections as to the trend of compensation for the following year to give hospitals a basis for anticipating such movement for budget purposes and taking appropriate action to maintain its competitive position in attracting qualified personnel in a rational manner, including sharing personnel shortages in a time of major expansion of healthcare facilities.

The early G-K reports made a recommendation that hospitals establish a four- or five-step salary range for each classification within the range to recognize time in service or special qualifications. In many respects this compensation pattern followed the civil service concept in government compensation and over a period of time there developed a reaction against what some considered to be a lockstep of automatic raises.

As a result of dissatisfaction and the increased professional status and experience of hospital personnel directors, by the 1980s there was a strong movement to eliminate the automatic step increases and go to a merit system with departmental merit pools and far greater emphasis on individual performance. However, with this change came an increase in individual employee grievances, requiring that each hospital not only establish a responsible grievance procedure as set forth in the current survey reports but also actually implement it.

These early reports projecting future trends to some degree became self-fulfilling prophecies. As a result of the expansion in the application of antitrust law to hospitals, particularly the nonprofit hospitals, our office subsequently advised the Hospital Council to eliminate the detailed projections as to future compensation and substantially limit the report to detailed analysis of existing patterns as well as reporting general projections of wage inflation and trends from outside the hospital field.

Another phase of great assistance to the industry was the development of a fringe benefit survey which not only reported on existing patterns but also gave assurance to hospital management, including the governing boards, of the availability of basic data upon which they could make their decisions. These efforts helped us develop a responsible compensation and personnel policy pattern for the industry. Evidence that it was well accepted by hospital personnel is the fact that currently only 20 percent of hospital personnel in the Southern California region are unionized and more than half of these are either Kaiser Permanente or county hospital employees, both of which were organized before this program was initiated.

❦ Hospital CEO Compensation

At the same time that major progress was being made in the general labor pool of hospitals, issues developed regarding executive compensation. In the 1960s it was the continuing pattern by hospitals not to disclose financial statements to the public nor make available the compensation paid to what is now denominated as the chief executive officer. Thus hospital governing boards recruiting a new CEO or reviewing the compensation for the existing CEO had no database to which to refer. There were none of the surveys in existence as there are now by the major accounting firms or the consulting organizations.

The title of superintendent was widely used for hospital chief executives when I first entered the field. Eventually this evolved to administrator, followed by consideration as to whether they would be a corporate officer such as a vice-president and a member of the board. I was committed to the need for the CEO to be either the executive vice-president or president, as well as being a member of the governing board. I was convinced the CEOs could be much more effective in dealing with the community as well as the hospital medical staff if they were a corporate officer and a member of the board of directors, as well as being adequately compensated for the immense responsibilities they carried.

With this in mind, I suggested to the Hospital Council Board it might be possible to do a confidential survey of CEO compensation practices through my office. As holder of the result I would be in a position to respond to confidential calls from any chair of a hospital board who was struggling with CEO compensation for a new hire or for a current CEO. This approach was authorized and I circulated a simple questionnaire to all of the hospital board chairpersons with an explanation of the purpose of the survey, promising that no individual hospital's response would be identified, but noting that only those who participated in the study could have access to the data. Amazingly, I got a large response which I then put on spreadsheets so I could report on the range of compensation by comparable size and programs of hospitals whenever I was called upon.

I received many calls from board chairpersons and had interesting discussions with them not only about compensation but also about job titles. I then asked them to keep me informed with changes so I could update my survey. I was interested that this informal request indicated a continued upgrading of the hospital administrator's role as many were advanced to either executive vice-president or president with more appropriate compensation.

In my discussions with hospital executives I also stressed how important I felt it was to have the president of the medical staff as an ex-officio board member. This was initially quite controversial. Many hospital governing boards resisted this suggestion, claiming conflict of interest problems, but I assured them that when an actual conflict existed it could be handled by the chief of staff disclosing the conflict and not voting. On the other hand, having the chief of staff on the governing board assured a direct line of communication between the hospital and medical staff and would avoid the misunderstandings and distorted rumors that otherwise plague the institution.

It is hard to believe now this was such a controversial issue. For these same reasons, I advocated the practice of having the hospital CEO, or a designated representative of the governing board, attend meetings of the medical staff and its executive committee, especially those dealing with quality of care and credentialing.

Salaries for hospital CEOs used to be secret

8

Emergency Care Liability Issues

T he California Medical Association and the California Hospital Association have been national leaders in jointly sponsoring legislation to modify the potential liability of care providers in the interest of assuring emergency care for patients in many different settings, both in and out of the hospital. This legislation fell under the general description of Good Samaritan Laws.

Our first proposal dealt with the public belief, which was true, that physicians and nurses avoided stopping at the scene of an automobile accident for fear of becoming involved in litigation due to the potential of a bad result in any care given without the usual resources available in the office or hospital. It was also believed that physicians refused to put any identification on their cars for fear of being called upon.

We had good leadership in the Legislature from Senator Byron Rumford, a pharmacist who was knowledgeable and sympathetic to problems of the medical profession. As a result in 1959 the Legislature under his leadership adopted the first Good Samaritan law in the nation, which now provides in Section 2395 of the Business and Professions Code:

§ 2395. **Care at scene of emergency** – No licensee, who in good faith renders emergency care at the scene of an emergency, shall be liable for any civil damages as a result of any acts or omissions by such person in rendering the emergency care.

"The scene of an emergency" as used in this section shall include, but not be limited to, the emergency rooms of hospitals in the event of a medical disaster. "Medical disaster" means a duly proclaimed state of emergency or local emergency declared pursuant to the California Emergency Services Act (Chapter 7 [commencing with Section 8550] of Division 1 of Title 2 of the Government Code).

Acts or omissions exempted from liability pursuant to this section shall include those acts or omissions which occur after the declaration of a medical disaster and those which occurred prior to such declaration but after the commencement of such medical disaster. The immunity granted in this section shall not apply in the event of a willful act or omission.

Questions were raised as to the extent of the exemption, particularly as to its application to what may be described as in-house emergencies, not only within a patient's room in the hospital but also within the emergency room itself. These emergency problems were complicated by the legal requirement of an informed patient consent for medical procedure. Fortunately, the California courts have been sympathetic to the problems of providing emergency care within the hospital under what we describe as Code Blue calls. (This is the announcement made on the hospital intercom and loudspeaker system to alert all hospital personnel and physicians to the existence of an emergency and the need for the emergency protocols to be put in effect.)

CMA and CHA worked with the state Legislature to clarify this issue by Sections 2396, 2397 and 2398 of the Business and Professions Code, adopted in 1980, which provide:

§ 2396. Emergency care for complications after prior care by another – No licensee, who in good faith upon the request of another person so licensed, renders emergency medical care to a person for medical complication arising from prior care by another person so licensed, shall be liable for any civil damages as a result of any acts or omissions by such licensed person in rendering such emergency medical care.

§ 2397. Emergency situations in licensee's office or hospital; failure to inform patient; causes; definitions –

(a) A licensee shall not be liable for civil damages for injury or death caused in an emergency situation occurring in the licensee's office or in a hospital on account of a failure to inform a patient of the possible consequences of a medical procedure where the failure to inform is caused by any of the following:

(1) The patient was unconscious.

(2) The medical procedure was undertaken without the consent of the patient because the licensee reasonably believed that a medical procedure should be undertaken immediately and that there was insufficient time to fully inform the patient.

(3) A medical procedure was performed on a person legally incapable of giving consent, and the licensee reasonably believed that a medical procedure should be undertaken immediately and that there was insufficient time to obtain the informed consent of a person authorized to give such consent for the patient.

(b) This section is applicable only to actions for damages for injuries or death arising because of a licensee's failure to inform, and not to actions for damages arising because of a licensee's failure to inform, and not to actions for damages arising because of a licensee's negligence in rendering or failing to render treatment.

(c) As used in this section:

(1) "Hospital" means a licensed general acute care hospital as defined in subdivision (a) of Section 1250 of the Health and Safety Code.

(2) "Emergency situation occurring in the licensee's office" means a situation occurring in an office other than a hospital used by a licensee for the examination or treatment of patients requiring immediate services for alleviation of severe pain or immediate diagnosis and treatment of unforeseeable medical conditions, which, if not immediately diagnosed and treated, would lead to serious disability or death.

(3) "Emergency situation occurring in a hospital" means a situa-

Health Policy – The Hard Way

tion occurring in a hospital, whether or not it occurs in an emergency room, requiring immediate services for alleviation of severe pain, or immediate diagnosis and treatment of unforeseeable medical conditions, which, if not immediately diagnosed and treated, would lead to serious disability or death.

(d) Nothing in this article shall be construed to authorize practice by a podiatrist beyond that set forth in Section 2473.

§ 2398. Aid to participant in athletic event or contest – No licensee who in good faith and without compensation renders voluntary emergency medical assistance to a participant in a community college or high school athletic event or contest, at the site of the event or contest, or during transportation to a health-care facility, for an injury suffered in the course of such event or contest, shall be liable for any civil damages as a result of any acts or omissions by such person in rendering such voluntary medical assistance. The immunity granted by this section shall not apply to acts or omissions constituting gross negligence.

There are also immunity sections placed in the California Governance Code dealing with emergency care in case of a major disaster, all designed to assure care in situations where the health-care provider is not working within the usual setting. All these are designed to prevent the fear of the tort system denying appropriate care by volunteer professionals to injured persons.

9

Standardized Procedures for Nursing

There has always been a love-hate relationship between the nursing and medical professions, particularly as related to expanding the practice of nursing. As a general concept and legally the physicians can do anything that a nurse is permitted to do, but the nurse cannot do everything that a physician can do. Thus there is an overlap which is controlled by definition of the practice of nursing in the Nursing Practice Act.

There has been a continuous expansion of nursing activities as physicians have abdicated their role in patient care both from the viewpoint of their personal convenience as well as to utilize their time more efficiently and increase their income. On the other hand, the nursing profession is very conscious that there are more and more services which they could perform but which are still restricted to physicians. Conflict is most acute as to the procedures that can be done under the order of or under the supervision of a physician as distinguished from being completely independent of physician supervision and control. Both by statute and by practice special areas of nursing have evolved such as the nurse anesthetist and the nurse practitioner.

An historical perspective on the methodology we developed to deal with this problem in the hospital setting highlights the issues which first arose from procedures such as intravenous blood transfusions, use of bed rails, declaration of death, institution of cardiopulmonary inhalation therapy, performing hemodialysis, specialized critical care, employee health programs, and the like.

During the 1960s I became increasingly conscious of the unhappiness of physicians with the fact that under the law, as it was being interpreted, only a physician could administer an I.V. This meant that in all hospitals, but particularly in smaller hospitals that did not have residents or interns on service, the attending physician had to leave his office practice or, more critically, get up in the middle of the night, to go to the hospital to start an I.V., a procedure which they believed a nurse could just as well perform.

I had begun to discuss this issue with Dave Willett, legal counsel for the California Medical Association, when we found an old California Supreme Court case in which two physicians had filed charges against a registered nurse who had administered general anesthesia which the physicians charged was in violation of the Medical Practice Act. The Supreme Court found that the nurse had followed a methodology that was generally recognized and accepted practice in hospitals, and that such nurses were performing their duties by carrying out the orders of the physician to whose authority they are subject, and thus did not violate the Medical Practice Act. We concluded that we could utilize this case as authority within a hospital to qualify specific nurses to perform what we chose to describe as "standardized procedures."

Next we brought together an inter-professional group from medicine, nursing and hospital administration to consider the issue. This gathering produced a series of joint statements approved by all three organizations dealing with the practice areas mentioned. Each joint statement spelled out the requirements for approving the procedure and the qualifications of the nurse to perform the specific procedure under protocol established by a joint committee composed of representatives of the medical staff, department of nursing and administration.

This process was so successful that the Legislature at the 1973-1974 session amended the Nursing Practice Act to authorize the development of standardized procedures not only at individual healthcare institutions but also at organized healthcare systems that are not a licensed healthcare facility. Section 2725 of the Business and Professions Code was amended as follows:

§ 2725. Legislative declaration; practice of nursing; functions

In amending this section at the 1973-74 session, the Legislature recognizes that nursing is a dynamic field, the practice of which is continually evolving to include more sophisticated patient care activities. It is the intent of the Legislature in amending this section at the 1973-74 session to provide clear legal authority for functions and procedures which have common acceptance and usage. It is the legislative intent also to recognize the existence of overlapping functions between physicians and registered nurses and to permit additional sharing of functions within organized healthcare systems which provide for collaboration between physicians and registered nurses. Such organized healthcare systems include, but are not limited to, health facilities licensed pursuant to Chapter 2 (commencing with Section 1250) of Division 2 of the Health and Safety Code, clinics, home health agencies, physicians' offices, and public or community health services.

The practice of nursing within the meaning of this chapter means those functions, including basic healthcare, which help people cope with difficulties in daily living which are associated with their actual or potential health or illness problems or the treatment thereof which require a substantial amount of scientific knowledge or technical skill and includes all of the following:

(a) Direct and indirect patient care services that insure the safety, comfort, personal hygiene and protection of patients; and the performance of disease prevention and restorative measures.

(b) Direct and indirect patient care services, including, but not limited to, the administration of medications and therapeutic agents, necessary to implement a treatment, disease prevention, or rehabilitative regimen ordered by and within the scope of licensure of a physician, dentist, podiatrist, or clinical psychologist, as defined by Section 1316.5 of the Health and Safety Code.

(c) The performance of skin tests, immunization techniques, and the withdrawal of human blood from veins and arteries.

(d) Observation of signs and symptoms of illness, reactions to treatment, general behavior, or general physical condition, and (1) determination of whether such signs, symptoms, reactions, behavior, or general appearance exhibit abnormal characteristics; and (2) implementation, based on observed abnormalities, of appropriate reporting, or referral, or standardized procedures, or changes in treatment regimen in accordance with standardized procedures, or the initiation of emergency procedures.

"Standardized procedures," as used in this section, means either of the following: (1) Policies and protocols developed by a health facility licensed pursuant to Chapter 2 (commencing with Section 1250) of Division 2 of the Health and Safety Code through collaboration among administrators and health professionals including physicians and nurses; (2) Policies and protocols developed through collaboration among administrators and health professionals, including physicians and nurses, by an organized healthcare system which is not a health facility licensed pursuant to Chapter 2 (commencing with Section 1250) of Division 2 of the Health and Safety Code. Such policies and protocols shall be subject to any guidelines for standardized procedures which the Division of Allied Health Professions of the Medical Board of California and the Board of Registered Nursing may jointly promulgate; and if promulgated shall be administered by the Board of Registered Nursing.

Nothing in this section shall be construed to require approval of standardized procedures by the Division of Allied Health Professions of the Medical Board of California or the Board of Registered Nursing.

It is my understanding that this procedure has now been adopted in many states as a method of dealing with the need for flexibility in effectively utilizing the skills of nurses. With the expansion of managed care and the creation of integrated medical groups we can expect that the role of the registered nurse will continue to expand into new areas, and that the use of standardized procedures will minimize the conflict between the professions in the Legislature. Anyway, more doctors will enjoy uninterrupted sleep and I am sure that the patients are better served. For myself, I have always preferred to have a specially trained nurse administer shots or start I.V.s than a physician–particularly an intern or resident.

The subject of nursing practice constrains me to express my views on the problems created by the proliferation of separate licensed categories of various functions within a hospital. Licensing has traditionally been applied to special skills for high tech procedures or operation of specialized and hazardous equipment used for diagnosis or treatment of patients. Such licensure is a two-edged sword, for while it is designed to assure the patient that only a prequalified individual will perform these limited procedures, it also creates a monopoly for a restricted group who can perform these activities. Over time as particular equipment or procedures become obsolete, the ability of the healthcare provider to adjust to new advancements and train personnel for multiple functions is limited and costly. How our railroad industry almost collapsed as a result of individual licensure and self-perpetuating groups locked in by labor contracts is a bad example of what could happen to the healthcare system.

In my role on behalf of hospitals I have long opposed the expansion of the various individual license categories–with limited success. I became intrigued with a concept first published by Professor Nathan Hershey at the University of Pittsburgh who proposed that in the place of individual license categories, healthcare institutions or entities such as a hospital or medical group be given a general license to perform necessary patient services and a part of its license requirements be to employ and train individuals to perform the function. The hospital or entity would be legally responsible for the conduct of the individuals, which is true under the doctrine of respondent superior for all employees.

Needless to say, organized nursing successfully led the battle against this innovation. Personally I would accept the continuance of nursing licensure as an exception to the proposal just as I admit the importance of having a broad definition of nursing to meet the continually changing needs for qualified personnel.

Hopefully, at some point in time, perhaps as a result of the restructuring of personnel roles and needs for true managed care, there will be the possibility of doing a comprehensive review of the whole complex of special license categories with the intent of combining or eliminating categories now obsolete or that interfere unnecessarily with the ability of the health system to utilize the skills of existing personnel in overlapping roles. Such a restructuring could include combining categories into what could be designated as a licensed healthcare technician who would have the basic skills and training adaptable to newly evolving specialties. This would be more at the level of a licensed practical nurse who, with minimum additional training, could be certified to fulfill identified needs without creating new licensed categories.

10

The Critical Role of the Medical Staff

❦ *Evolution of the Medical Staff in California Facilities*

When I first started to practice law in 1940 the hospital medical staff was a rather unsophisticated organization. In many respects it was organized and operated as an old boys club. The basic organization document was two or three pages long and was entitled "Constitution and Bylaws of the ‒‒‒‒‒‒‒ Hospital Medical Staff."

The contents covered the organizational features – description of the governing board and officers, time and place of meetings, plus a short section on qualifications for membership, which were rather simple requirements including the existence of a valid license, a degree from an accredited medical school, being a person of good moral character, competency to practice medicine, letters of recommendation from three members of the medical staff (generally based on a lunch meeting in the hospital cafeteria), and lastly, of most importance, a requirement that the individual be a member of the local county medical society.

Upon obtaining approval of the medical staff, an actual appointment was made by the governing board of the hospital and in the early days there was no delineation of privileges – these did not develop until required by the JCAH at a later date. Great reliance was placed on membership in the county medical society which, of course, had its own elementary standards. There was none of the in-depth review of the candidate's history such as occurs now, in part because hospitals were relatively small and the doctors knew each other. Typical is the response I received when I asked a chief of staff why a particular physician was not renewed during the annual medical staff reappointments. He simply said, "I knew he was not a good doctor." That was all it took.

However, as the specialization of medical practice evolved, membership on a medical staff became increasingly important to the individual physician and the need to limit practice to qualified persons in the various specialties became critical for the hospital. The whole process was subject to potential abuse by physicians already on the staff desiring to protect their turf coupled with the need to protect patients from substandard practice.

Hospital governing boards continued to rely on medical society membership; however, the role of the county medical society itself became increasingly controversial and subject to litigation. We finally advised hospitals that this provision be eliminated to avoid charges of conspiracy between the county medical society and individual hospitals, thus placing the total responsibility of physician credentials on each individual medical staff and hospital governing board.

In my experience the principal difficulty with credentials was always the mediocre doctor who did not deliberately cut corners but who was just not up to snuff in maintaining skills or medical knowledge. I also found that often the mediocre if not altogether bad physician tended to have outstanding physician/patient relations. Their patients loved them because of the attention and tender loving care they received, because the incompetent physician covered for any deficiencies with tender loving care which contrasted with the arrogance of more highly qualified peers. I had experience with a number of rural hospital disciplinary actions in which the community of patients rose in organized protest against any action we proposed to take against their loved physician. In those days of a physician shortage we considered it the role of the medical staff to rehabilitate below-standard physicians rather than cut off their practice.

With the rapid expansion of hospitals in California to meet the needs of a burgeoning population following World War II, there was a corresponding increase in situations where individual physicians were either denied admission to a medical staff or were refused annual renewal of membership on a staff. As a matter of prudence as hospital attorneys, we recommended to hospital medical personnel that the less risky procedure was to avoid a midterm suspension or termination of medical privileges and wait for the annual renewal before removing a physician whose performance was considered no longer acceptable.

As a practical matter this worked for a number of years as there was then no legal requirement that a physician was entitled to due process on the denial or renewal of privileges. It functioned particularly well when we had good hospital medical staff leadership that would work with the problem of the physician who had personality problems such as alcohol abuse or was seriously disruptive in relationships to other hospital personnel or physicians, this often coupled with a lack of basic competency.

Frequently I was called on to help the medical staff committee handle an individual physician, to identify a problem and take "corrective action" as distinguished from punishment. We would suggest that a physician, depending on the nature of the difficulty, seek medical help (usually psychiatric analysis and care) or, if indicated, take a leave from the staff for additional medical education. This process enjoyed a high degree of success and we saved many physicians in this manner. It was my personal philosophy that when we failed to save a physician we had failed to do our job, discipline being the last resort. Unfortunately, as hospital medical staffs became larger and more complicated this process was less effective. Medical staffs began imposing more severe remedies, including suspension or termination of privileges on the subject physician, and in turn the disciplined physicians challenged the medical staff in the courts.

The early litigated cases by disciplined physicians were mostly in Northern California, primarily in district hospitals. The reason for this was that there were many more district hospitals in Northern California, particularly in the suburban area around San Francisco Bay, and as quasi-public hospitals they were subject to stricter legal principles requiring them to make their facilities available to members of the public, including physicians.

The earliest reported case was that of *Dr. Wyatt v. Tahoe Forest Hospital District*, 174 CAL. APP. 2D 704 (1959), concerning a physician who had applied for medical staff membership which was denied based on conduct and proceedings by the board of medical examiners some ten years prior to this application. A request for a hearing on this application was denied and the physician went to court on the issue.

Although the hospital prevailed in the trial court, the appellate court reversed the decision ruling that a district hospital was required by statute to adopt rules and regulations for the operation of the hospital including admission to the medical staff. The appellate court held that not only were the hospital's rules and regulations vague and ambiguous but that the applicant, on denial, was entitled to a hearing to assure he had not been treated in an unreasonable, arbitrary, capricious or discriminatory manner. The court did hold that a physician, merely because he has a license to practice medicine, was not automatically authorized to practice medicine in a public hospital, but was subject to reasonable rules and regulations.

The appellate court in the *Wyatt* case found that hospitals' bylaws which stated that the standard for medical staff membership was "that only physicians and surgeons, whose background, experience, and training insures, in the judgment of the Board, that any patient would be given the best possible care" were subject to the whim and caprice of the hospital directors. Therefore that standard was inadequate. It also held that the denial must be for an existing cause and that matters which had occurred ten years previously were not controlling. This then became the new law in California and followed a developing pattern across the other states.

My role was to argue the case in the appellate court on behalf of the hospital which, as can be seen, was not entirely successful. This was the prelude to many litigated cases that followed in which we attempted to create a public policy balance between the protection of patients on the one hand and the rights to practice by the individual physician on the other. Although later there was legislation on these issues, the original health policy requirements relating to medical staff appointments, renewals or corrective action were established by the courts.

There followed a whole series of cases involving district hospitals. The California Supreme Court in the 1962 case of *Rosner v. Eden Township Hospital District*, 25 CAL. RPTR. 551, deemed the requirement that an applicant be "temperamentally and psychologically suited for coöperative staff hospital functions with other members of the medical staff and with other hospital personnel" was beyond the authority of the hospital. The standard applied should be based on technical competence, character and ethics.

In *Martino v. Concord Community Hospital District*, 43 CAL. RPTR. 255 (1965), the court held it was appropriate to require a

physician who had not had staff privileges in any hospital for almost ten years to submit to written and oral examinations but that
the inquiry would be limited to factors of technical competence.

In *Rosner v. Peninsula Hospital District,* 38 CAL. RPTR. 392
(1964), the medical staff bylaws required medical staff members to
carry malpractice insurance or, as an alternative, deposit $300,000
cash with the hospital as proof of ability to respond to a claim for
injury to or death of patients treated. The requirement was adopted as an emergency regulation and was apparently in anticipation
of an application for medical staff privileges by Dr. Rosner. The
court held that the requirement was an invalid delegation of authority to deny privileges to a private body (the malpractice insurance company) without adequate safeguards against arbitrary or
self-motivated action.

The *Rosner* case remained the law of California until 1974
when the Legislature, at the urging of the California Hospital
Association, adopted Section 1319 to the Health and Safety Code
providing that:

> The rules of a health facility may include provisions that require
> every member of the medical staff to have professional liability
> insurance as a condition to being on the medical staff of the
> health facility.

The legislative history of this section states that one of the purposes of the enactment was to overrule the Rosner case.

Section 1319 was enacted the year before MICRA was adopted
and right in the middle of a sweeping medical liability crisis in
which a number of carriers were withdrawing from the medical
liability insurance field. Premiums for insurance still available for
both physicians and hospitals were soaring. Many physicians were
dropping their insurance and soon the Truck Insurance Exchange,
principal carrier for hospital liability insurance, reported a major
increase in hospital losses as the result of hospitals being forced to
pick up the entire load of defense and liability charges in cases

where the hospital was sued jointly with an uninsured doctor.

Due to the added risk of uninsured physicians, TIE had proposed that any hospital not requiring all its medical staff to have medical malpractice insurance pay a surcharge on its own premium. Although the CHA insurance committee was sympathetic, it did not recommend this approach, particularly in view of the *Rosner* case, but rather urged that CHA support legislation to clarify the *Rosner* ruling which had led to the adoption of Section 1319 of the Health and Safety Code previously mentioned. The CMA supported this proposal, and thus nearly all hospitals, with approval of their medical staffs, adopted such a requirement on the rationale that it was necessary to protect all of the medical staff from the potential of being sued jointly with and because of an uninsured physician.

As anticipated, application of the statute was challenged as unconstitutional and as being an improper delegation of power to an independent entity, but the case of *Wilkinson v. Madera Hospital*, 192 CAL. RPTR. 897 (1984), sustained the statute as being constitutional. Also the court held that the hospital could reasonably define the qualifications of the insurance company as being an admitted carrier and found the minimum of $500,000 coverage was reasonable. Approval of this requirement was important, as the lack of financial viability of some of the insuring entities the doctors proposed to use was amazing. The court also held that this requirement did not violate the federal Medicare statute assuring freedom of choice of physician.

Meanwhile the Legislature had not been inactive on the continuing controversy of medical staff privileges. Assemblyperson Nicholas Petris on March 22, 1963, introduced in the state assembly AB 2031 which he titled the Fair Hospital Practices Act. This bill proposed the State Department of Public Health be authorized and directed to promulgate rules and regulations for protection of doctors from unfair and unreasonable discrimination with respect to medical staff membership or the exercise of medical staff privileges in hospitals. In addition, the department would formulate statewide standards for medical staff membership and privileges that were fair, reasonable and objective.

Individual hospitals could set higher standards as long as they did not contravene the purposes of the act. The department was also to set out fair, reasonable, definitive and objective grounds for termination of staff privileges, establishing model procedures. Of equal importance, the bill would guarantee a hearing for aggrieved doctors before the hospital governing board, who, if not satisfied with the hearing, could apply for and receive a *de novo* hearing before the State Board of Public Health. The act would apply to all hospitals "supported wholly or in any part by charitable contributions solicited from the general public." Thus it did not apply to private profit-making or governmental hospitals.

This proposed legislation received violent opposition from both the CMA and the CHA. Fortunately this legislation came before the public health committee which had held hearings in 1957 on hospital medical staff abuses that led to joint CMA and CHA development and implementation of the "Guiding Principles for Physician/Hospital Relations," discussed later. It should be emphasized here that it was as a result of the joint action by the CMA and CHA in facing up to the issues and initiating a positive program to protect both patients and physicians that led to the defeat of this legislation, in spite of the fact that somewhat similar legislation had been previously adopted in the state of New York as the result of a pattern of alleged discrimination against physicians who had affiliated with a health insurance plan or medical group.

Even though the legislative battle was won with the defeat of AB 2031 in 1963, litigation continued unabated. In 1968 Dr. Stanford W. Ascherman brought a comprehensive action charging a conspiracy to deny him hospital practice privileges against the San Francisco Medical Society, the Franklin Hospital, St. Joseph's Hospital, French Hospital, American Mutual Liability Insurance Company and numerous individuals associated with those entities, reported in 32 CAL. APP. 3D 627 (1974). Apparently the genesis of the dispute arose out of an occurrence at the Press Club where Dr. Ascherman expressed strong support for national universal health insurance. Dr. Ascherman contended that because of this, his memberships in the medical society and the medical staff of the hospitals were terminated without due process. In a lengthy opinion the district court reversed the trial court's decision in favor of certain of the defendants, and in particular the medical society and the hospitals, and required that the matter go back for a new jury trial, and that Dr. Ascherman was entitled to due process hearings at each of the hospitals and medical society.

The hospitals, however, continued to fight with Dr. Ascherman, and on February 24, 1975, the district court of appeal, at 45 CA. 3D 507, in *Ascherman v. St. Francis Hospital,* a hospital not involved in the earlier case, held that the medical staff bylaw requirement that an applicant to the medical staff submit three letters of reference from active members of the hospital medical staff was invalid. Dr. Ascherman had submitted 23 letters of reference but none from active members of the hospital medical staff. As a result his application was returned without being processed or Dr. Ascherman being given a hearing. The appellate court reversed the trial court decision and directed the trial court to issue an injunction compelling the hospital to reconsider the application under a fair procedure, as outlined by the court.

Many more cases followed these, particularly against private hospitals, as the courts continued to refine the duties of the hospitals. Although the courts subsequently placed additional burdens on the hospitals, neither the courts nor the Legislature has ever chosen to grant hospitals the right of subpoena in a medical staff hearing context. It would appear that such a right should be available in the interest of fairness in view of the heavy burden placed upon the medical staff in the hearing procedures required.

A good example of the difficulties a hospital faces in dealing with credentialing issues of the medical staff occurred at the Fresno Community Hospital during this period. I got a call from the hospital administrator reporting that a neurosurgeon whose privileges had been terminated had sued the individual members of the medical staff executive committee for $50,000 for defamation and interfering with his practice of medicine. What made the problem unusual as well as serious was the fact that when the defendant doctors requested a legal defense from their individual professional liability carriers, at least two of the carriers denied coverage and refused to defend.

Fortunately, the American Mutual Liability Insurance Company, the official county medical society-sponsored carrier that insured most of the doctors, tendered a defense, but there were still a number of physicians who had no insurance protection. The hospital then submitted the case to the Truck Insurance Company, which responded that the hospital liability policy coverage applied to the hospital board of directors and officers but not to the medical staff officers and directors and initially denied coverage. Needless to say, there were some unhappy doctors who had unfortunately discussed the medical staff discipline of the plaintiff doctor at the local country club.

Our review of the conflict found that the matter had been handled very professionally at the medical staff hearing level. Since there were no other neurosurgeons on the medical staff to perform a review of the surgeon's practice the judicial review committee pulled the last 50 patient charts of the accused doctor and sent them for review to the dean of the University of Michigan Medical School, who in turn had a panel of neurosurgeons review them. They reported back that after a careful analysis, they found that the practice of the physician in question was seriously below standard with substantial injury to a number of the patients. Based on that report the medical staff had terminated the doctor's privileges.

We were in immediate touch with Messrs. Hassard and Willett as to the insurance coverage issue. As it happened, the California Hospital Association was having its annual meeting at Yosemite. We called a special meeting of the CHA insurance committee, who reviewed the matter and recommended, because of the potential serious impact on the peer review process, that TIE should provide the defense for those physicians not otherwise covered. This was discussed with the TIE representative.

We knew there was no hospital coverage of medical staff committee members, as such, under the TIE hospital policy; however, I suggested that TIE consider these physicians as volunteers under the hospital volunteer coverage language. TIE agreed and provided a defense to the otherwise uninsured doctors. The matter was ultimately resolved without any liability being found. One of our problems was that the physician in question was quite prominent in medical organization matters and was scheduled to be an important speaker at the next CMA annual meeting. As a result of this case, the physician-sponsored carriers nationwide have amended their policies to provide coverage for physicians performing their medical staff administrative duties. The TIE policy has also been amended to provide backup coverage.

Later we had a series of malpractice cases in the Sacramento area involving Dr. John G. Nork, another neurosurgeon. This was complicated by charges from the patients' attorneys of a hospital and medical society coverup. The newspaper publicity about him led to an increased media demand that hospitals be held liable for the acts of physicians even when they were independent contractors. During the furor some 80 medical malpractice cases were filed against the doctor. In reviewing these cases we were surprised that a substantial number of victims were either nurses or other hospital personnel who should have known of his deficiencies. We thus found no evidence of a coverup. However, it was clear that there was reluctance of the medical staff to appreciate the seriousness of the charges and that the physician in question was effective in convincing patients they were well served by his "tender loving care."

Although such medical staff cases were dramatic, receiving widespread media attention, they were just the tip of an iceberg of matters being handled on a routine basis at the various hospitals throughout the state. It is the medical staff investigations and hearings that furnish the basic protection to the public of the qualification and performance by physicians. Licensure is only a rough screening process and does not deal effectively with the problem of the mediocre physician. The unrecognized heroes of this process are the individual physician members of the medical staff who serve as volunteers on the judicial review committees – without compensation for hundreds of hours, generally at long night meetings – to hear and determine matters brought before them. Not only are these difficult decisions to render, but they often can become extremely contentious and emotional.

Although in recent years I have not acted as legal counsel to such committees, I had more than my share during the 1960s and 1970s. Based on my experience, over half of the physicians brought before the judicial review committees had a basic personality problem, often quite severe. Even though it was discretionary with the committee whether or not legal counsel for the physician should be permitted to participate in the committee hearings, the general practice was to do so. Often, it seemed, the legal counsel selected by the subject physician did the doctor's cause more harm than good. Generally the attorney chosen was experienced in litigation, frequently a specialist in medical malpractice cases and tended to take a strong adversary position instead of working to settle the matter. As a result, the committee unconsciously ended up trying the attorney and not his client.

In a number of cases it was my impression that the doctor's

attorney literally destroyed the client's chances by antagonizing the committee members who, as physicians, basically distrusted lawyers. More recently there has emerged a number of attorneys who specialize in representing physicians in disciplinary matters who are more sensitive and realistic in their approach to the judicial review committee. My experience has been that physicians who used as their advisor at the hearing a well-respected physician member of the medical staff achieved the most desirable result by either a favorable decision or a negotiated settlement.

11

Peer Review

As litigation against physicians and hospitals relating to medical-staff privileges heated up, both CMA and CHA were deeply concerned about maintaining the peer review process on a voluntary basis without protection from liability for those participating in the exercise. Thus the two associations collaborated in drafting and pressing for a series of legislative actions.

The first legislation dealt with the potential liability of the participating members of the peer review committee and was adopted in 1961. This, I think, was the first such legislation in the country. The pertinent language as it now appears in the current Section 43.7 of the civil code is:

> § 43.7. Immunity from liability; mental health professional quality assurance committees; professional societies, members or staff; peer review or insurance underwriting committees; hospital governing boards –
> (a) There shall be no monetary liability on the part of, and no cause of action for damages shall arise against, any member of a

duly appointed mental health professional quality assurance committee that is established in compliance with Section 4070 of the Welfare and Institutions Code, for any act or proceeding undertaken or performed within the scope of the functions of the committee which is formed to review and evaluate the adequacy, appropriateness, or effectiveness of the care and treatment planned for, or provided to, mental health patients in order to improve quality of care by mental health professionals if the committee member acts without malice, has made a reasonable effort to obtain the facts of the matter as to which he or she acts, and acts in reasonable belief that the action taken by him or her is warranted by the facts known to him or her after the reasonable effort to obtain facts.

(b) There shall be no monetary liability on the part of, and no cause of action for damages shall arise against, any professional society, any member of a duly appointed committee of a medical specialty society, or any member of a duly appointed committee of a state or local professional society, or duly appointed member of a committee of a professional staff of a licensed hospital (provided the professional staff operates pursuant to written bylaws that have been approved by the governing board of the hospital), for any act or proceeding undertaken or performed within the scope of the functions of the committee which is formed to maintain the professional standards of the society established by its bylaws, or any member of any peer review committee whose purpose is to review the quality of medical, dental, dietetic, chiropractic, optometric, acupuncture, or veterinary services rendered by physicians and surgeons, dentists, dental hygienists, podiatrists, registered dietitians, chiropractors, optometrists, acupuncturists, veterinarians, or psychologists which committee is composed chiefly of physicians and surgeons, dentists, dental hygienists, podiatrists, registered dietitians, chiropractors, optometrists, acupuncturists, veterinarians, or psychologists for any act or proceeding undertaken or performed in reviewing the quality of medical, dental, dietetic, chiropractic, optometric, acupuncture, or veterinary services rendered by physicians and surgeons, dentists, dental hygienists, podiatrists, registered dietitians, chiropractors, optometrists, acupuncturists, veterinarians, or psychologists or any member of the governing board of a hospital in reviewing the quality of medical services rendered by members of the staff if the professional society, committee, or board member acts without malice, has made a reasonable effort to obtain the facts of the matter as to which he, she, or its acts, and acts in reasonable belief that the action taken by him, her, or it is warranted by the facts known to him, her or it after the reasonable effort to obtain facts.

"Professional society" includes legal, medical, psychological, dental, dental hygienic, dietetic, accounting, optometric, acupuncture, podiatric, pharmaceutic, chiropractic, physical therapist, veterinary, licensed marriage, family, and child counseling, licensed clinical social work, and engineering organizations having as members at least 25 percent of the eligible persons or licentiates in the geographic area served by the particular society. However, if the society has less than 100 members, it shall have as members at least a majority of the eligible persons or licentiates in the geographic area served by the particular society.

"Medical specialty society" means an organization having as members at least 25 percent of the eligible physicians within a given professionally recognized medical specialty in the geographic area served by the particular society.

As originally adopted the section did not include most of the wide variety of specialty societies now included who later asked to be added. However, the legislative policy of this section as relating to medical staff and related organizations was essential to protect the new review process in the best interest of patient care.

In 1984 Section 43.8 was added to the civil code to give immunity to those who provided information to the peer review committees—a necessary addition to obtain continued coöperation from anyone in the litigation atmosphere of California. This section provided that:

... there shall be no monetary liability on the part of and no cause of action for damages shall arise against any person on account of the communication of information in the possession of such person to any hospital, hospital medical staff, professional society, medical or dental school, professional licensing board or division, committee or panel of such licensing board, peer review committee or underwriting committee described in Section 43.7 when such communication is intended to aid in the evaluation of the qualifications, fitness, character or insurability of a practitioner of the healing arts and does not represent as true any matter not reasonably believed to be true. The immunities afforded by this section and by Section 43.7 shall not affect the availability of any absolute privilege which may be afforded by Section 47.

As the peer review system became more effective, attorneys representing malpractice plaintiffs sought access to the proceedings of the committees. Again the CMA and CHA concluded that unless the activities of these committees were protected, physicians would be reluctant to participate in anything that might encourage or support potential medical malpractice actions against their fellow doctors. "There but for the grace of God go I."

The first response to this was the passage in 1965 of what is now Section 1156 of the Evidence Code prohibiting introduction into evidence in a civil suit any committee records, including interviews, reports, statements or memoranda relating to its studies. However, as adopted it did not prohibit the discovery of such materials; this created a big loophole in its effectiveness. This weakness was soon realized and so the CMA and CHA obtained passage in 1968 of what is now Section 1157 of the Evidence Code, which provided:

> (a) Neither the proceedings nor the records of organized committees of medical, medical-dental, podiatric, registered dietitian, psychological or veterinary staffs in hospitals or of a peer review body as defined in Section 805 of the Business and Professions Code, having the responsibility of evaluation and improvement of the quality of care rendered in the hospital or for that peer review body or medical or dental review or dental hygienist review or chiropractic review or podiatric review or registered dietitian review or veterinary review or acupuncturist review committees of local medical, dental, dental hygienist, podiatric, dietetic, veterinary, acupuncture or chiropractic societies or psychological review committees of state or local psychological associations or societies having the responsibility of evaluation and improvement of the quality of care shall be subject to discovery.
> (b) Except as hereinafter provided, no person in attendance at a meeting of any of those committees shall be required to testify as to what transpired at that meeting.

Health Policy – The Hard Way

(c) The prohibition relating to discovery or testimony does not apply to the statements made by any person in attendance at a meeting of any of those committees who is a party to an action or proceeding the subject matter of which was reviewed at that meeting, or to any person requesting hospital staff privileges, or in any action against an insurance carrier alleging bad faith by the carrier in refusing to accept a settlement offer within the policy limits.

Although heavily attacked by the plaintiff's attorneys, this section has been generally successful in protecting the committee records from discovery. One very limited loophole was developed in the protection in a 1986 case of *West Covina Hospital v. Superior Court*, 41 CAL. 2D 846, in which the California Supreme Court held that the section did not preclude a committee member from testifying voluntarily about the proceedings of the committee. In that case one of the physicians on the committee was so incensed at what the committee uncovered that he insisted on testifying against the physician subject to the disciplinary matter at a subsequent malpractice case against the subject physician. Although we were concerned about this loophole, actual experience has indicated that this pattern has not been a repeated occurrence.

Recently another loophole has been established by the California Supreme Court in the case of *Arnett v. Dal Cielo*, 401 CAL. 4TH 267 (1996), in which the court held that the protection against discovery under 1157 did not apply to the State Medical Board in its investigation into possible physician misconduct. Although disappointing, it is our opinion that this will not be a major deterrent to medical staff peer review activities. However, the case does demonstrate the difficulties inherent in drafting legislation that is going to be subject to such intensive scrutiny.

An unresolved issue with 1157 has been whether a hospital in defending a malpractice case can waive the prohibition and use the committee findings as a defense in an action brought against the hospital for failure to properly monitor its medical staff physicians. We, on behalf of CHA, as well as the CMA, have taken the position from a policy point of view that the integrity of 1157 is so important that hospitals should not attempt to waive the immunity even though it might be to the hospitals' advantage in a particular case in which it was charged with failure to properly screen or supervise a particular physician. This conclusion is based on our long experience that if we are to encourage a frank and forthcoming evaluation of another physician's conduct, the physicians performing the evaluation must be protected against disclosure of their viewpoint; otherwise they will not effectively perform in fear of being subject to a variety of litigation and harassment.

In August, 1995, the *Los Angeles Times* published an in-depth article under the headline, "Boy's Death Cracks the Shell of Privacy." What followed was a comprehensive investigative report on a tragic death at Denver's St. Joseph Hospital of an eight-year-old who failed to survive a relatively simple ear and face surgery. The report detailed the fact that the death was the result of the failure of the anesthesiologist to stay awake and appropriately monitor the vital signs during the course of a surgery in which the surgeon was not in a position to do so as he was operating with a microscope. The reporter was able to substantiate that there had been past incidents in which this anesthesiologist had dozed off in surgery. These had been duly reported, but no action had been taken because of what the article described as the medical world's Code of Confidentiality. The article was well researched and very critical of the failure of the medical staff and the hospital administration to protect patients from such misconduct.

Such stories gives one pause as to the justification of the legislative immunities established by legislation such as Section 1157 that mandates the confidentiality and immunity of physicians and others who participate in peer review, credentialing and other quality of care procedures within the hospital. This is a tough policy issue and the protections provided can only be justified if the medical professionals and healthcare institutions earn their protection by proper performance.

I am also reminded of a telephone call I received at home one Sunday evening from a young administrator at a small rural hospital north of Bakersfield. The thrust of the call was, first, to apologize for calling me at home on the weekend and then to report an incident at this small hospital with a total medical staff of five individuals. The caller also reminded me that I had been a vocal advocate of peer review and control, which did not appear to apply in this situation in which his two surgeons were off on a fishing trip and the chief of staff was severely intoxicated in the emergency room. All I could do was advise the administrator to get the chief out of the emergency room and put it in the control of the nursing supervisor. I promised to get on the matter first thing Monday morning – which I did.

After discussing this with Mr. Hassard and Mr. Willett in their capacity of legal counsel for the California Medical Association and with their full coöperation, the CMA and the local county medical society immediately assembled a team of three medical leaders experienced in rural medicine who went to the hospital, met with the five members of the medical staff and the administrator and worked out a mutually satisfactory solution.

This was only one of many times over many years of practice when either I or members of our office have had such prompt coöperation from Mr. Hassard, Mr. Willett and the CMA in organizing teams to go into a particular aggravated conflict involving a hospital and/or medical staff and work to develop a solution. You do not achieve resolution like this through the bureaucratic procedures of licensure. As the Denver case indicated, no process is perfect when we are dealing with human conduct in the complex decision-making functions of medical care. We have to work on it every day and provide the necessary tools, support and protections to make it work. However, patients are not left without a remedy if the voluntary system does not work. In the case of *Elam v. College Park Hospital*, 132 CAL. APP. 3D 332 (1982), the district court of appeal held that:

> We can perceive of no reason why this established duty of due care does not encompass the duty asserted by *Elam*, for, as a general principle, a hospital's failure to insure the competence of its medical staff through careful selection and review creates an unreasonable risk of harm to its patients.

This case does not hold that the hospital is automatically jointly liable for the medical malpractice of an independent medical practitioner, but that it may be held liable for its failure to properly credential and select the individual physicians. For the future we can assume that similar liability may be imposed upon managed-care plans for similar failure in credentialing their panel physicians. Likewise, the managed-care plans or the large integrated medical groups will preëmpt the historical role of the hospital medical staff as well as the hospital governing board.

Peer review and voluntary controls, particularly at the medical staff level, have their issues, but based on many years of experience the thrust of our effort must be to improve the system; I see no other effective alternative. Later, when we deal with managed care, I will discuss my hopes that managed care, with its emphases on outcomes and prevention, will enhance the effectiveness of peer review through the use of financial incentives as well as improved data on individual physician performance.

National health policy on the importance of peer review has been emphasized by the creation of the National Health Provider Data Bank to which must be reported information about disciplinary action on physician and other health professionals, including medical staff actions as well as malpractice judgments. The information in this federally established data center is available to credentialing mechanisms such as medical staffs and managed-care organizations to enhance their quality control decision-making. We supported a similar reporting in California – with one important difference from the federal act in the threshold reporting figure of medical malpractice cases as $50,000 for hospitals and $30,000 for physicians so as to encourage small settlements including provision of continuing care. However, we can expect there will be continued agitation by consumer groups for more public access to the data bank. This is a tough health policy issue.

Both physicians and patients have a major stake in the maintenance of quality healthcare. This is a people business and requires the voluntary efforts of all participants to develop procedures and mechanisms that will not only define quality but will also assure that it is provided by qualified practitioners. The challenge to the healthcare providers is guaranteeing the public that their healthcare practitioners are qualified. This responsibility extends through the entire feeding chain of healthcare.

I must also point out that the voluntary medical staff structure described here is a distinctive American approach. In Europe, for example, there is a pyramid structure with a boss at the top who wields complete authority. From anecdotal reports I understand this approach is not nearly as effective in assuring quality of care, and serious medical malpractice problems are being identified.

12

Insurance & Malpractice

S hortly after joining Musick and Burrell in 1940 I had my first
educational experience in dealing with hospital insurance
matters. Mr. Burrell was general counsel to the California
Hospital Association as well as Blue Cross, The Lutheran Hospital
Society and other healthcare organizations. He sent me to San
Francisco with Ritz Heerman, superintendent of the California
Lutheran Hospital, to meet with the rating bureau of the National
Board of Fire Underwriters and discuss a separate fire-rating classi-
fication for hospitals distinct from other institutions such as nurs-
ing homes, retirement homes and the like.

Mr. Heerman was one of the most dynamic leaders the hospital industry ever produced and this was an example of his leadership not only on behalf of his own hospital, a part of the Lutheran
Hospital Society, but all hospitals. He was convinced hospitals
were paying more than their fair share for fire insurance because
they were in a rating group that included other institutions whose

buildings were at a far greater fire risk than hospitals.

Not only were hospital buildings more substantial but, more importantly, they operated on a 24-hour basis with patient-care personnel active all day and night and thus, automatically, the entire hospital was always under surveillance for possible fires. With considerable effort Mr. Heerman had been able to develop statistics to prove his case and he had been granted a hearing before the fire rating bureau, which would decide the merits of the case. The bureau had taken the position that there were not enough hospitals or hospital premiums to justify the separate rating.

My role was simply to be with Mr. Heerman, primarily as an observer. We went up to San Francisco on the night train (no airplanes then) and met in the imposing board room. Mr. Heerman made his case in a most impressive manner and achieved a favorable result, which over the past half century has saved many millions of dollars, initially for California hospitals, and later for hospitals nationally. The lesson I learned that day was that a well prepared presentation, carefully documented, was necessary to obtain movement by such resisters of change as the insurance industry.

About the same time Mr. Heerman became concerned with the number of reported incidents of burned feet of females in the ObGyn ward following their delivery. His investigation satisfied him that the cause was related to nursing staff efforts to comfort their patients who complained of cold feet – not uncommon following anesthesia. It was customary for nurses to put hot-water bottles at the foot of the bed. However, in their desire to better serve their patients, nurses would sometimes fill the hot-water bottles with water they heated over a Bunsen burner at their nursing station, resulting in the burning of their patients' feet. Based on this report Mr. Heerman ordered all hot-water bottles removed from the hospital to be replaced by plastic bags filled with silicone which were warmed in controlled-temperature heaters.

Another problem was identified when the California Hospital

was sued and held liable for mixing up babies in the nursery. As a result Mr. Heerman developed and initiated the procedure of taking footprints of each newborn immediately after delivery to establish identification. The use of fingerprints was not feasible for many infants but it was possible to get a good footprint.

Patient identification also caused concern because the wrong patient could be delivered to surgery or improperly prepared for surgery. This happened because patients were identified by the medical chart located in a rack at the foot of the bed, but sometimes the beds would be shifted and the wrong chart would follow the patient. To avoid this problem Mr. Heerman developed the wristband identification system now universally followed. Even that was not foolproof unless it was combined with the nurse reading the identification from the band and requiring the patient to respond orally as well. Our incident reports indicated that the greatest chance of misidentification came from switching two people with the same unusual name. The nurses were much more careful in checking on a common name such as Smith or Jones.

World War II brought a clear suspension of my experiences with insurance. Not until after the war did I return to these challenges. Jane and I bought our first house on Fox Hills Drive just east of the Fox Studios, in what is now the Century Plaza and Marriott Hotels. One day waiting for the bus to my office downtown I met a Mr. Dean Nusbaum, who turned out to be the number two man in the J.H.R. Nettleship Company–the brokerage organization that had created the group program for the Los Angeles County Medical Association and several other nearby county societies, as well as the national insurance program for the American Osteopath Association. Obviously we had much in common to discuss on our daily trip downtown.

Dean suggested to Mr. Nettleship that I be employed as corporate legal counsel to the company, which then occurred. So I became, to some degree, involved in its management and was able to observe the trials and tribulations of dealing with physicians on the delicate subject of medical malpractice. When Mr. Nettleship was taken ill, I was designated to be acting president of the company, in which capacity I had to approve all major settlements proposed by the defense counsel – an eye-opening experience.

Based upon my subsequent encounters with malpractice problems, I now realize how unique the Nettleship Company was. For example, it had developed a specialized legal defense program called the American Physicians Defense Bureau under the supervision of an experienced trial attorney, Mr. John Allen. This was both an effective and efficient approach to the problem of keeping control of the quality and the cost of defense. Also, as a specialized group they were best able to deal with the problem of the distrust and hatred by physicians for attorneys, including the insurance company attorneys.

It worried me that the defendant doctors did not consider the insurance company as their partner in solving their common problems, and subsequently there was little loyalty shown by physicians for their own insurance programs which they would dump any time for a reduction in premium, making it difficult to work on long-range solutions to the malpractice issues. This experience prepared me for the challenge of developing the California Hospital Association medical liability plan, which I will discuss shortly.

In 1949 Mr. Heerman began working with Ed Ekdahl, an insurance broker who was developing two group hospital insurance proposals – one for hospital medical malpractice initiated by a group of 18 hospitals primarily in the Los Angeles area, the other a workmen's compensation program. Mr. Heerman was concerned not only about the cost of insurance and the high commissions being charged (generally 20 percent) but also the fact that usually the insurance was placed through a broker who was on the hospital board of directors.

However, Mr. Heerman and Mr. Ekdahl made one critical

mistake. The malpractice coverage was placed with the two carriers controlled by a Mr. Stuart Hoppes of San Francisco. About a year into the program, both carriers were declared insolvent by their respective state insurance commissioners and Mr. Hoppes reportedly fled to Tunis.

The workmen's compensation insurance had been placed with the Industrial Indemnity Company, a responsible organization, but the program was attacked by the California Insurance Commission on the grounds that there was no authority under the insurance code for the creation of an employer-group workmen's compensation insurance plan. In fact, the insurance industry was doing its best to discourage group compensation insurance and it was not until the law was amended at the urging of the California Hospital Association that it was possible to initiate another proposal.

Mr. Heerman did not give up. He went east to contact directly such major carriers as Aetna, Travelers and Hartford and solicit their interest. He also encouraged local brokers to see what they could offer and in the process created a strong insurance committee through the California Hospital Association to work with him.

Finally all was prepared to consider selection of a new broker and carrier. Presentations were to be made to the committee prior to the 1953 annual meeting of the CHA in Santa Barbara. I was assigned the role of working with Mr. Heerman and the committee in reviewing the proposals. Our preliminary study indicated that of the four submissions, only the one submitted by George Walker, a broker on behalf of the Aetna Insurance Company, was viable. However, 48 hours before the scheduled approval meeting Aetna notified Mr. Walker it was withdrawing its proposal. George Walker, a most resourceful person, was able within the 48-hour period to convince the Truck Insurance Exchange, part of the Farmers Insurance Group, to substitute as the carrier in what had been the Aetna proposal. In fact, because of time pressure, Aetna's name was still on the papers when they were submitted to the committee.

The proposals of the other three carriers were dismissed by the committee as being without substance and then they carefully reviewed the Truck proposal, which was very innovative. However, neither the Farmers Insurance Group nor the Truck Insurance Exchange had ever insured malpractice risks. On the other hand, the Truck Insurance Exchange (TIE) had done a remarkable job insuring long-haul trucks which had become almost uninsurable because of the terrible truck wrecks on the interstate highways. TIE had initiated a hard-nosed safety program of both training and policing the drivers so as to substantially reduce the risk and, in effect, became a partner with the major trucking companies in dealing with these issues. This record impressed the CHA committee, which authorized Mr. Heerman and myself to negotiate an arrangement with Mr. Walker and the TIE.

Fortunately, Mr. Walker had the full confidence of the TIE as he had arranged with Lloyds of London their excess insurance cover which had been the key to the TIE's growth. TIE believed it could develop the same kind of safety program for hospitals that it had for trucking. It is with this background that Mr. Heerman, Mr. Wenzel, president of TIE, and his assistant, Ken Tyler, worked with Mr. Walker and myself in developing not only an exceptional contractual relationship between TIE and CHA but as a second step developed a totally new insuring agreement that was the key to creating what was, in effect, a partnership between TIE and CHA in resolving the many liability insurance problems of hospitals.

The Truck Insurance Exchange was a separate free-standing entity, incorporated as a reciprocal under California law. In effect it was owned by its policyholders, who selected the board, which, prior to the new arrangement, were representatives of the trucking industry. Under the new arrangement CHA was given the right to elect one director. Truck Underwriters, a wholly owned subsidiary of the Farmers Insurance Group, had a management agreement with TIE and is a for-profit organization. It receives a percentage of premiums for its services which includes both the premium tax and the brokerage commission, ultimately payable to the Sullivan/ Kelly organization, the successor to George Walker after he retired. Farmers Insurance Group, as a public-listed corporation, receives its income from its ownership of the Truck Underwriters.

Through the combination of a group insurance contract between TIE and CHA and a new form of insurance policy, this liability insurance arrangement broke ground for many new creative goals. As Mr. Heerman sought, there was in effect a partnership between the insured hospitals on the one hand and TIE on the other, all working to achieve better quality of care and more cost-effective liability insurance. The most important new concept was that the insurance coverage was for all hospital liability risks except those specifically excluded under the policy terms, such as for automobiles, certain nuclear energy provisions and the like. This meant any new tort liability that developed would be automatically covered rather than needing new endorsements to the policy.

Such coverage was very important when new issues such as wrongful termination, failure to provide cardiac resuscitation, and others, emerged over time. Rather than having five or more specialized insurance policies with possible gaps and conflicting overlaps, which was the industry pattern prior to this time, there was now only one insurance carrier on the risk. In practice, the premiums would be adjusted as new risks were identified. Also, the hospital policy continued to run without annual renewal negotiations, often a controversial matter before the hospital board of directors, so long as the hospital paid its premium. The policy was terminable by either party on three month's notice.

The premium itself was to be a level premium for all hospitals, based upon units of service, such as occupied bed days, outpatient procedures and inpatient procedures such as surgeries. Initially there was no experience rating, as it was Mr. Heerman's strong belief that we were dealing with industry-wide issues which should be shared by the entire industry working together on prevention and quality of care. He also fully recognized the randomness of the malpractice claims dilemma. The premium could be adjusted by Truck on 90 days' notice after prior consultation with the insurance committee of CHA. The committee would have access to the TIE experience figures as well as the right to use its own actuary or accountant to review the information. This process became particularly important as the claims frequency and severity escalated in the build-up to the 1975 malpractice crisis.

Under the agreement TIE was required to employ an individual experienced in hospital administration to supervise the risk prevention activities, including on-site inspections of hospitals on an indepth basis. That person would report back to the CHA committee any identified matters that it should consider. The committee was authorized to hold hearings on errant hospitals and to institute corrective action including possible termination from the program for failure to coöperate. Coöperation was the key, not just the existence of claims. The policy coverage was also unique for that point in time as it not only included the hospital but also its board of directors, officers, employees and volunteers.

As part of the partnership concept any disputes between TIE and the hospital or its employees as to whether or not a particular claim would be settled or litigated was to be referred to a subcommittee of the CHA insurance committee which had authority to act. The fact that the hospital would not be penalized by an individual increase in premium for bad experience meant that the committee could act based upon what was best for the program as well as the industry. If, for example, the nature of a particular claim indicated the claim could be settled rather than go to trial and risk creating a possible bad precedent in the courts without penalizing the individual hospital on its future premiums, this was done.

Although deductibles were being used by the insurance industry (primarily as a way of eliminating nuisance cases or as a penalty on the hospital or physician), a wholly new approach was developed based on my experience in dealing with hospitals and doctors who believed the insurance company would settle within the deductible regardless of the merits. Our new procedure created a $100 flat deductible to handle such matters as lost property, broken dentures and the like. Beyond that, a shared deductible up to an agreed amount (usually between $500 to $50,000) divided 50/50 by the insured hospital and TIE, comforted the insured with the knowledge that the carrier was bearing part of the loss. As the size of the deductible increased this became more and more useful.

Ritz Heerman insisted that there be an exclusive brokerage arrangement so that the amount of the premium going for that purpose could be minimized. Under the insuring arrangements at the beginning, TIE carried the first $20,000 of each loss and the balance was covered by excess insurance up to one to five million based on the wishes of the individual insured.

The brokerage commission on the TIE share was negotiated by Truck Underwriters and was just under two percent of the TIE premium. The commission on the excess insurance was 15 percent. This compared with the standard retail commission then of 20 percent of all of the premiums. About two-thirds of the premium was for the primary and one-third for the excess, although this changed over time. To partially offset the opposition from the brokerage community, many of whom were on hospital boards, the CHA group workers' compensation program negotiated with the Argonaut Insurance Company continued to recognize participation of local brokers, but with a reduced commission.

With this new sophisticated program in place the insurance committee of CHA became the prestige committee of the association – a committee on which past presidents of CHA often asked to serve. One of the first major developments was recruiting Jack Fulton, an individual with experience in hospital administration, to head up the safety program – a program intended to lower insurance costs by reducing the number and severity of hospital incidents. Jack had been assistant administrator at Pomona Valley Community Hospital and was also trained as a lawyer, though he was not a practicing attorney in California. He spent a lot of his time at the California Hospital working with Ritz Heerman to identify difficulties that needed to be resolved. It was Jack who initiated an incident reporting system to be implemented by all participating hospitals.

Prior to this, most medical malpractice carriers would treat an incident report as a claim report and automatically set up a charge against the hospital's experience for the cost of setting up a file. Needless to say, this charge discouraged reporting. Under the new system no charge was made and, further, a hospital that did not have a record of filing a substantial number of reports was suspected of not being aware of what was going on. It became the assumption of the insurance committee that no hospital could be so perfect. As the committee became more experienced, it directed Jack to bring before them hospital executives and even hospital board members to explain why there were few incident reports.

Working with Mr. Heerman on claims-prevention activities, Jack first zeroed in on the matter of sponge counts in surgery. He reviewed the claims files at TIE and observed actual operations in progress in an effort to establish a possible solution to the problem. He noted that the universal practice was for there to be two sponge counts – one performed by the instrument nurse just prior to the commencement of surgery, the second performed when the surgeon, having finished the procedure, began to close the wound. Apparently it was assumed there would be little sponge activity after that point. However, there were still sponges being left in patients – some even with the hospital name on them.

After this review Jack recommended to the insurance committee that the practice be changed to include a third sponge count made prior to skin closing. This change was made and was almost completely successful in eliminating the problem. Since final closure had not been finished it was possible for the surgeon to open the patient up if it was determined there was a missing sponge.

Agitation developed from surgery nurses to mandate instrument counts on the same pattern. This became a continuing question as a result of a California appellate court decision involving the Watsonville Community Hospital in which the hospital was held liable jointly with the surgeon for leaving an instrument in the surgical field. The court held that although it was not the community practice to require or perform instrument counts, the negligence was so apparent that the hospital should be held jointly liable.

This was referred to Jack, who after study reported to the insurance committee that the number of instrument cases was small. He felt the delay in finishing surgery and continuing anesthesia caused by an instrument count would do harm to more patients than would the rare instrument left, even if the hospital were responsible. Based on this advice plus their experience, the insurance committee refused to order formal instrument counts prior to closing and asked Jack to work with the surgical nurses so they would be more alert to possible missing instruments. The CHA committee was attacked in nursing journals and by the American Association of Operating Room Nurses, but the committee held its ground.

Later, when I reported this story at a legislative hearing as evidence of hospital concern for patient care as being more important than liability the association was commended by the legislative committee. It should be noted that injury to a patient from a lost sponge was much greater than from a lost instrument, as the sponge increases the development of scar tissue resulting in a potentially serious adhesion problem. On the other hand a lost instrument may do relatively little harm to the patient.

A similar case was Jack's advice on the use of bed rails. When he did his initial study nearly all hospital beds were those big awkward iron structures to which metal bed rails had to be attached by hand. It was also necessary for nurses to hand crank the bed down in order to install the rails. To complicate matters further, it was the custom that bed rails could not be raised without orders from the attending physician. The situation was particularly aggravating at night in multiple-bed rooms (and most rooms then had at least four beds) when the nurse or attendant, after getting authorization from the physician, then dragged the bed rails out of the closet and inserted the metal rails with all the racket that ensued.

Jack recommended to the insurance committee that nurses be given the authority to order bed rails–resulting in legal liability responsibility being transferred from the attending physician to the hospital. His study established that the large number of patient falls out of bed involved a variety of factors: If the patient fell out of a bed without rails, it often meant a free fall to the hard floor with potential head or hip injuries. But if the patient was climbing over the rails, the patient unconsciously clung to the rails and would slide to the floor but was rarely severely injured. Therefore the appropriate use of rails was an essential safety factor even if the legal responsibility was transferred from physician to the hospital.

Following this study Jack strongly encouraged hospitals to install electric beds to relieve the nurses of having to use antiquated cranks and to use beds with half rails so the patient could scramble out around the end of the rail rather than free falling from the bed. Jack determined that a sedated patient who felt the urge to get out of bed would do so regardless of the consequences. Of equal importance, falls out of bed (or, as Jack recommended it be charted, "out of bed without permission") were one of the most frequent causes of patient injury and eventual claims. This change to half rails produced statistical improvements that were phenomenal.

The most frequent disability occurrence in hospitals were slip-and-fall cases. Jack's studies determined that hospitals were using on floors the kind of wax that associated cleanliness with being bright and shining – but such floors were also the most hazardous. He found that a no-skid wax was available and started a campaign for its introduction. Since there was no instrument available to test the slipperiness of floors, Jack instituted what we called "the silk handkerchief test." By wrapping a brick in a silk handkerchief, he could attach this to ordinary fish scales. By pulling the brick with the fish scale he could get a rough reading on the slipperiness of the floor and make his point to hospital personnel on how to maintain floors and, above all else, keep them dry.

However, these issues paled by comparison with the blind-baby problem that was an increasing phenomenon in hospitals. Mr. Heerman, in working on the situation with some other hospitals, developed studies that finally substantially resolved the matter. They found out that the cause of the condition known as retrolental fibroplasia or infant-eye damage was caused by excessive oxygen in the incubators used primarily for premature infants, who were particularly susceptible to permanent or serious blinding. The problem was caused by the relatively primitive construction of the incubators so there was no way the nurses in the nursery could determine the oxygen concentration in the incubator. As the pediatrician would order oxygen by liter flow, when faced with the issue of possible death of the infant the doctor tended to err on the side of maximizing the oxygen flow to the distressed baby. The results were potentially catastrophic in a well-sealed incubator.

Because of studies performed at the California Hospital and elsewhere, it was determined by the insurance committee that all liter flow instrumentation should be removed and oxygen concentration meters used instead. This was ordered on a crash basis and Jack and I were instructed to conduct patient-safety workshops throughout the state to pass the word and sell the hospitals on the necessity for action. Within a year this assignment was completed with favorable results, and I can recall only one case of twins, one of which was blinded and the other one not, in a hospital in which there was a delay installing the concentration meter due to the demand we had created in the market.

The largest insurance case we had in the first five years of the plan involved a blood transfusion error in which incompatible blood was transfused into the son of a former governor of Arizona. This happened in an Arizona hospital that was in the program as a result of its relationship with a California patient organization. In any event, the case was eventually settled for $50,000, which was a blockbuster settlement in those days.

This highlighted the question of incompatible blood and as a result Jack worked with my partner, Joe Saunders. They developed all kinds of prototype devices in an attempt to make the process of taking blood fail-safe clear through to an actual transfusion. However, the final solution was a major tightening up of the internal procedures within the hospital to prevent accidental mismatching. In any event, a review of the statistics indicates there was a steady decrease in the number of transfusion errors of all types. These are just a few examples of the results of Jack Fulton's pioneer work in creating the industry-wide, risk-management program for hospitals.

13

Malpractice Prevention Workshops

L ooking back in history it is clear that the rapid expansion of new, improved and far more complex surgical procedures in hospitals was a major contributor to the increase in frequency and severity of malpractice claims against physicians and hospitals. The information developed by Jack Fulton in the 1960s and the workshops he presented throughout the state to educate physicians and hospitals on liability issues and preventive procedures were significantly lowering the frequency of the more common claims. However, the insurance committee of the CHA was not satisfied that all was being done that could be. To a great extent it was preaching to the choir and we were not getting the message through to those who were making the errors.

A query was referred to Jack Fulton, Joe Saunders and myself asking us to come up with a new approach. In our opinion it was necessary to handle this on a multidisciplinary basis where we could work directly with known individuals rather than through specialty organizations. In my experience, when you involve a specific medical specialty organization, asking it to designate individuals to join with others on a problem-solving mission, the process is often doomed to failure. Those selected by the society as representatives might be strong politically, but they were not necessarily the highly motivated, truly dynamic practitioners within that particular segment of medicine. Furthermore, those selected invariably felt they had to go back to the specialty society for instruction on particular issues so that the society, in effect, exercised a veto power over actions. Also such representatives often took little or no interest in the project and their attendance and participation level was low.

As a solution, we suggested that a small planning committee screen the participants selected. This led to Joe Saunders' proposal that we name the project "California Invitational" from a successful prototype in the field of golf. Thus the individuals would be carefully selected for their clinical practice knowledge and their ability to work with others and would be carefully briefed on the importance of their participation. To achieve our purpose we proposed that the process should come from the grassroots up rather than from the top down as is the usual pattern in organized medicine.

As our 1969 invitation stated, the "Invitational" workshops would seek to find ways to alleviate malpractice issues by confronting the pertinent and practical matters related to the everyday provision of healthcare by a multidisciplinary group consisting of physicians, hospital administrators, nurses, defense attorneys, insurance executives and others who could make a contribution.

Based on Jack Fulton's studies as well as the experience of the small planning group, the agenda for the workshops was developed to cover eight specific high-risk areas: 1) Elopement and suicide, 2) Anesthesia, 3) Surgical cardiac arrest, 4) Emergency and floor cardiac arrest, 5) Requirements for qualification of assistants in surgery and surgical privileges, 6) Infection control, 7) Maternal and neonatal injuries, and 8) Infection injuries.

Basic material was developed for the use of the workshops, and chairpersons were selected for each, with responsibility placed on the chair to develop a specific agenda to produce the goals for the final report. It was emphasized that it was not the purpose of the workshops to determine standards of practice as such, even though it was recognized that based on validity and acceptance of the recommendations they could individually become community standards of practice. Rather, their purpose was to allay the adverse knee-jerk reaction of physicians to any development of cookbook medical practice and the potential liability for failure to follow the cookbook. This was to be a program to determine a process for decision making, not a new set of rules and regulations. Ultimate decisions on implementation would revert to the medical staffs.

There followed 17 malpractice prevention workshops throughout California, each one divided into the eight section topics. The daylong meetings ended with the total group discussing the individual section's recommendations. Representatives from each workshop were selected to come to a unifying session in a three-day meeting in Palm Springs where all the recommendations were reviewed by each section with a final report made to the general session. When the consensus was published, the final document was presented to all interested parties, who were invited to two information meetings, one in San Francisco, the other in Los Angeles.

The final report was organized into the eight topics with a series of specific suggestions as to conduct of care to be developed in each hospital to prevent malpractice occurrences. To a substantial degree these represented what we now call "protocols" or "best practice guidelines." Because of the broad involvement in the workshop strategies the steering committee was convinced the process was most productive and was repeated in the California Invitational II, which was dedicated solely to injuries to the newborn. This was a risk management approach on a multiprofessional basis that achieved its results as a part of the process and not just a statement that collected dust. The entire report, published in *California Medicine* 112:89–97, March 1970, emphasized the importance of doctors and hospitals working together in the best interest of patient care.

In spite of the success of the original California Invitational project, liability matters from claims in one particular area alleging neonatal brain damage rapidly increased in both numbers and severity. Russ Clark, the claims manager for the Truck Insurance Exchange, suggested we propose to the California Hospital Association and the California Medical Association that they jointly sponsor a California Invitational II project dealing solely with the problems of neonatal brain damage injuries with the objective of initiating a major injury-prevention program statewide.

The following chapter reprints an article I authored which describes this project, "Using Malpractice Claims Data to Successfully Attack the Problem of Infant Brain Damage." In California Invitational II's final report, it was suggested that CMA and CHA update the recommendations after two years experience. Three years later in discussions with Russ Clark and Gail Harshaw at Truck Insurance Exchange, we realized that the issue of infant brain damage had not been completely solved and although much progress had been made the healthcare providers should take another look at it.

I contacted Brad Cohen, M.D., chair of Invitational II, who enthusiastically supported the request for CMA and CHA to sponsor an update jointly. Unfortunately, changes in CMA leadership caused a bad case of medical politics and turf warfare. Evidently physicians active in the American College of Gynecology strongly objected to any action by the CMA board, so CMA refused participation, which effectively killed the proposal. Now as I review jury reports on medical malpractice decisions, the frequency of major judgments for infant brain damage continues to be a severe problem. Unquestionably, the ACOG did a good job on practice standards for its ObGyn members, but I still wonder if we would not have been better served with another multidisciplinary California Invitational III.

14

Using Malpractice Claims Data to Confront the Problem of Infant Brain Damage

❦ *The Obstetrical Care Environment in the 1980s*

Although medical malpractice claims alleging liability for infant brain damage have always been one of seven or eight major sources of judgments and settlements against physicians and hospitals, it was not until the late 1970s and early 1980s that these claims rapidly increased in both size and number until in some areas of the country by the mid-1980s they were the number one problem. This evolution was the result of major advances in obstetrics, perinatal and neonatal intensive care. What happened was that those infants that previously failed to survive, because of a wide variety of injuries or congenital conditions, now were kept alive by new procedures and high tech equipment combined with ethical pressures to preserve the life of the traumatized infant regardless of the long-term consequences.

Unfortunately, a significant number of these infants' lives were severely compromised both physically and mentally. These same infants, often with genetic or congenital anomalies or intrauterine infections, frequently had additional difficulties during labor, delivery and the neonatal period. Since most of these infants were premature, their lack of full development exposed them to additional hazards and also complicated the environment in which their delivery or care was provided. The families of these infants were faced with the potential of long-term extraordinarily expensive care for possible neurologic deficits, such as cerebral palsy, mental retardation and seizures from multiple causes occurring before, during and, at times, long after birth, coupled with major physical deformities. Often these costs were not covered by private insurance and the families were faced with reliance on public sources.

Although such problems were often diagnosed or otherwise anticipated in advance, many of the consequences were unanticipated by the family and the attending physician. A major contributing factor was that many of the mothers had little, if any, prenatal care, so the delivery often was under emergency conditions. For these reasons, both preventable and non-preventable accidents could occur that might or might not have been responsible for the tragic results.

The ultimate care of these damaged infants could continue for an extended period and be extraordinarily expensive. In addition, their individual ability to provide for their own economic support when mature might be compromised. All of these factors contribute to the potential of boxcar recoveries in the event that fault by way of medical malpractice could be established. If tried for alleged medical malpractice, the cases are uniquely complicated and have an emotional content that makes them a high risk from a defense point of view. Further, there are often conflicts in observations between the hospital and the various professionals who are defendants as to causation issues. From the viewpoint of the family dealing with the emotional shock, the often overwhelming burden of future care is a critical factor. The emotional factors are complicated by possible feelings of guilt or the natural desire to strike out at those who could possibly in any way have contributed to the catastrophe.

Historically, the practice of obstetrics by both obstetricians and family practitioners had always been considered to be one of the happiest and most satisfying parts of medical practice. With the development of the neonatal brain damage cases, a wave of fear went through the practice. As a result, many obstetricians limited their procedures to gynecology and many more family practitioners withdrew totally from the deliveries.

At the same time that this change occurred, there were also alterations or attempted modifications by way of tort reform. Although started in the mid-1970s, but only to a very limited extent in many states, by the mid-1980s the consequences were very spotty and far from uniform. The reforms that would have furnished relief to healthcare practitioners in the neonatal brain damage cases were particularly controversial. These included the cap on pain and suffering that was adopted in only about one-half of the states and was the reform most vulnerable to constitutional attack, and the change in the collateral source rule, which permitted evidence of the existence of other sources of funding to deal with the economic losses of families of brain damaged infants. From the viewpoint of continued medical care, there were sources of relief through a variety of state and federal programs, but other economic factors, such as ability to be self-supporting, were lacking.

From observing the defense of alleged medical malpractice in infant brain damage cases, I realized that the problem was complicated further because these matters had evolved over such a short period of time and because the medical research and data as to causation, standard of practice and understanding of the basic etiology of these cases was not well understood or effectively provable in a court of law, even in cases which in retrospect were defensible. Thus the prudent approach was "when in doubt, settle," and there were plenty of cases in doubt.

❦ Malpractice Claims Data and Infant Brain Damage

For the year 1981, the GAO reported that obstetricians constituted 5.2 percent of all physicians practicing in the United States. However, in the GAO study of all malpractice claims for the year 1984 (these would be claims for occurrences in 1981–1983 because of the delay in claims filing), it was found that 12.4 percent of all malpractice claims filed involved obstetricians, the most of any specialty group. Of these, 45 percent resulted in some recovery for the claimant as compared with a success rate of 31.8 percent for all malpractice claimants. The average indemnity payment for cases involving obstetricians was $177,509, more than double the average payout for the 17 other specialty areas surveyed. Of greater importance, the total payment for obstetrical claims was 27 percent of the total dollar amount of all payouts, even though the obstetrical cases involved only 10 percent of the number of lawsuits.

Between 1982 and 1984 the average obstetrician premium increased from $10,946 to $20,818. By 1986, premiums had increased to $30,507 and by 1989 to $38,138, according to the 1990 ACOG study. By 1989, the average paid loss for a brain-damaged infant had reached $596,823, with half of all infant brain damage claims bringing a payment of $200,000 or more.

The impact on the availability of obstetrical services was increasingly serious. In the 1987 ACOG survey, 27.1 percent of the respondents reported reducing their practice of high-risk obstetrics, 12.4 percent reduced their number of deliveries and 12 percent left the practice of obstetrics. There was also a substantial drop in the number of medical students preparing to practice obstetrics. With increased insurance costs and the reduction of practitioners, the financial ability of many mothers to obtain obstetrical care was adversely affected. This was compounded because the number of family physicians willing to perform deliveries was shrinking rapidly. In many states the payment for obstetrical service for Medicaid beneficiaries was less than the unit cost of malpractice insurance.

Due to a serious deterioration in the malpractice insurance market in Virginia by 1986, 140 of 600 obstetricians were without coverage when an adverse decision of a federal district court declared the Virginia one-million-dollar cap on non-economic damages unconstitutional in an $8.3 million dollar judgment case involving infant brain damage. The remaining carriers commenced a withdrawal from the market. To meet this crisis, the Virginia Legislature adopted its Birth-Related Neurological Injury Compensation Act to establish a no-fault fund to provide for all medical, rehabilitative and custodial expenses, together with reasonable attorney fees and a wage stipend at age 18. The act included offsets for collateral sources and the administration followed a workers' compensation administrative format. A similar plan was adopted by the Florida Legislature in the following year. Both acts included some provisions for research and prevention with other steps to increase the availability of obstetrical care. They were funded by an assessment against the physicians and hospitals and dealt primarily with the symptoms of the problem relating to the cost and availability of malpractice insurance rather than the underlying problems of the causes and treatment of the injuries. As an alternative to the Virginia and Florida approaches, using no-fault cerebral palsy insurance has been suggested.

This was the situation that existed in 1982 and thereafter throughout the country and explains the impetus for the development and implementation of the joint project of the California Medical Association and the California Association of Hospitals and Health Systems.

❦ California Invitational II – Neonatal Brain Injury Prevention

The genesis of this joint project by these two associations along with a group of hospital and physician liability insurance carriers arose from the continued study of hospital claim patterns by Russell L. Clark, LL.B., the chief claims administrator for the Truck

Insurance Exchange, a California company that from 1953 had administered and insured the group program for the California Hospital Association and in the 1980s insured more than 250 hospitals in California.

By 1982, Mr. Clark was increasingly concerned with the rapid increase in the frequency of reported infant brain damage cases, as well as by the extraordinarily large size of the payments by way of settlement and judgments. The next year the number of such claims reached 32, increasing to 63 in 1984 and 78 in 1985. The Medical Underwriters of California, a major northern California underwriter of professional liability coverage, reported in a statewide study that in 1986 there were 22 judgments or settlements in excess of $50,000 for alleged birth injuries with a total paid indemnity of $73,286,528. This was an increase from 13 in 1985 and, more alarmingly, the indemnity cost per case for which indemnity was paid increased from $1,083,237 in 1984 to $1,929,886 in 1986, or a 78 percent increase in two years.

From the viewpoint of the insurance companies, these figures were even more threatening because data on the number of claims paid and the amount paid lags several years after actual occurrence. This meant each carrier was faced with the fact that its inventory of claims in process or, even more critically, the claims not yet made because of the extended statute of limitations for infant brain damage cases (eight years in California), if continued, would lead to extraordinary losses for the future to the point that physicians engaged in obstetrical practice would no longer be insurable.

Clark personally reviewed all of the claims files and consulted with Marvin Cornblath, M.D., from the department of pediatrics of the University of Maryland School of Medicine, a nationally-recognized expert in neonatology cases. It was their preliminary conclusion that with an intensive study of the claim files reported to the carrier it might be possible to identify the high-risk pregnancies as well as the treatment errors that led to the injuries.

Equally important was identifying those unique factors that led to injury from causes beyond the control of the healthcare provider. They concluded that far more information was needed than would be found in the usual liability claim file and authorized an additional study through the claims representatives so that, whenever possible, information was obtained retroactively as to the social history of the patient and the patient's family relating to smoking, alcohol utilization, drug abuse, nutrition patterns and other lifestyle factors that might contribute to the problem. Most of the information as to the medical care of the patient was available through the hospital and physician's records but this, too, was expanded by alerting physicians and hospitals to the importance of clarity on these cases and the need for additional information.

With this material in hand, and the quality of reporting continuing to improve, Clark and Cornblath identified more than 100 variables that could possibly contribute to the existence of a high-risk pregnancy or to a treatment problem that could indicate corrective or preventive practices. Each chart and additional data was correlated on spreadsheets. Based on the pattern, a determination was made to the causal factors involved as well as to the cases that could be defended or settled.

Based on the data then available, it was determined that 31 percent of the claims were classified as preventable, 42 percent were classified as non-preventable, and the balance were indeterminate because of the complexity of the circumstances or the lack of needed recorded medical information and family history.

Clark and Cornblath were convinced that this unique database could be used for further analysis by additional experts on a multiple disciplinary basis to make recommendations to the hospital-physician community on preventive actions necessary to attack this problem at its source.

At this point I became deeply involved in developing the resources and strategy to modify the pattern of care in order to attack the problem on a statewide basis. Our first step was to assemble a panel of experts to review the data and validate or modify the conclusions suggested by Clark and Cornblath. In selecting the panel, we chose physicians in the community who had outstanding reputations from the viewpoint of both their academic achievements and their acceptance in the medical community as active practitioners. As a part of the strategy in making the selections it was decided not to go to the national or local professional specialty societies for physicians to serve on the advisory committee.

The reason for this resolve was that those individuals selected to represent a specialty society have a real or implied obligation to obtain an official approval of their recommendations and this may delay or dilute the creativity of the suggestions. Obviously, the persons selected were individuals who were fully respected by their professional peers even though they were not bound to follow the official positions of their respective societies in dealing with treatment issues.

The advisory committee thoroughly reviewed the data and recommendations and made many suggestions that were incorporated into a proposed paper. The next decision to be made was to design an effective strategy that would have a positive impact upon pre- and post-natal care. It was determined that to be effective, far more than the mere publication of a paper would be required, even though publication of the paper in a respected peer- reviewed medical journal would be required as the first step.

The approach taken by the authors in preparing the paper was first to select from the schedule a definitive list of risk factors predictive of unfavorable outcomes. Out of the more than 100 possible risk factors, 27 were identified based on a review of spreadsheets, literature review and the experience of the panel members. Included in the list were such factors as sex of the infant, maternal demographic characteristics, maternal medical history, past obstetrics history, review of the course of pregnancy, the intrapartum course and the neonatal course. Not included in the broad population risk factors generally accepted in the literature were three factors that seemed particularly significant for this group of patients – mothers who had previous abortions (26 percent), prior admissions for false labor (16 percent), and the number of infants transferred to neonatal intensive care units (45 percent).

In addition to those three additional risk factors, most of the high-risk causes were associated with poor pregnancy outcomes and were significantly increased in the study group. Of particular significance were maternal obesity (200 pounds or more), diabetes, bleeding, twins, breech presentation, prematurity (less than 35 weeks gestation), post-maturity (42 weeks or more), prolapsed cord, low one- and five-minute Apgar scores, and birth weights (five pounds or less or more than ten pounds). Also included were neonates "floppy" at birth, evidence of seizures, congenital infections, and malformations.

The data was abstracted on a spreadsheet to determine the frequency of each risk factor for the 250 cases. These results then were compared with the expected frequency based on other accepted studies, including the data from the 54,000 children reviewed in the collaborative perinatal project of the National Institute of Neurological and Communicative Diseases and Stroke, and from the study of 3,326,632 live births as published for 1977 by the Office of Health Services Research. Based on a comparison of the general population frequency with the frequency found in the 250 cases, a risk ratio was computed for each of the risk factors.

The existence of combinations of these risk factors varied so widely that Clark and Cornblath utilized some subjective evaluation of the importance of the various combinations on a case-by-case basis for determining the cases that were preventable and, if so, by whom. Criteria were established for determining how each case should be classified as preventable, non-preventable, or indeterminate, as follows.

Preventable included actions or inactions taken by the mother, parents, obstetrician, family physician, midwife, anesthesiologist, nurses or pediatrician that clearly contributed to the neonatal course and outcome of the affected infant. Examples include:

- mother or parents refusing consent for timely Cesarean birth,
- misapplication of mid or high forceps resulting in skull fractures and aural hemorrhages,
- pronouncing infants dead who later were revived and survived,
- inadequate treatment of infection in one twin, but not in the other,
- inexpert ventilatory management inducing bilateral pneumothoraces.

Non-preventable included cases where the untoward outcome or clinical course could not have come from any specific action or inaction taken during the perinatal period. In addition, those conditions for which no known prevention or treatment is or was available at the time of the birth have been included here. Examples include:

- late onset of abnormal neurologic behavior following a completely uneventful pregnancy, labor, delivery and neonatal course,
- congenital anomalies,
- unavoidable, non-induced prematurity (less than 35 weeks) or extremely low birth weights in both average-size-for-gestational-age and small-size-for-gestational-age infants,
- complicated pregnancies associated with difficult conceptions, early bleeding, and multiple infections, often viral, unexplained catastrophic events occurring during labor or delivery, non-preventable congenital (TORCH [toxoplasmosis, rubella, cytomegalovirus, herpes]) or perinatal infections.

Indeterminate included those cases that contained insufficient information, multiple factors or conflicting reports that made it impossible to determine the events that were associated with or responsible for the outcome. Examples include:

- events related to pregnancy, labor, and delivery were unrelated to outcome, but no record or report of care from the neonatal intensive care unit was available,
- multiple injuries claimed, but examination at age three or four years showed no significant abnormalities,
- poor pregnancy history, complicated delivery, multiple congenital anomalies, and an intrapartum maternal death,
- conflicts among the delivery record, the nursery record, and the intensive care records relating to critical events during labor, delivery, Apgar scores, nursery course, and the like,
- claims that certain equipment, staff, operating rooms, or physicians were or were not available and in attendance at the time of delivery.

From the viewpoint of future malpractice cases, the findings as to which risk factors were not preventable established a database and checklist for claims analysis in determining the cases that might be defensible and the cases that should be settled. In addition, the results indicated critical weaknesses and gaps in the information that should have been developed during the entire course of patient/ physician hospital encounters. A general conclusion was drawn to the effect that many cases that had theretofore been treated as not defensible could be defended. Although this consequence had been a motivating factor in the initiation of the study, what really became important to all of us who participated was that there was a wealth of information developed that could be used to prevent or minimize the occurrence of these tragic incidents, regardless of who might be at fault.

With this potential in mind, the authors of the paper then concentrated on evaluating those risk factors that would permit intervention at any point to reduce the frequency and severity of neonatal brain damage, with preliminary recommendations as to remedial and preventive courses of conduct to be followed. In this regard, the paper concluded with the following delineation of early warning factors that should alert the appropriate healthcare providers as to potential problems and possible action that might be taken. The paper stated:

1. Prolonged gestation (more than 42 weeks), which may be associated with an increase in neonatal morbidity and mortality, can be avoided by precise dating of the last menstrual period, when possible, and the use of ultra sound, stress tests and tests of fetal maturity to determine the optimal time of delivery.

2. Mid or high forceps were used twice as often in preventable as in non-preventable cases (22 percent versus 11 percent), suggesting that the indications for their use should be precisely defined and limited to experienced physicians.

3. Cesarean delivery, which has been recommended to prevent damaged infants, was either an emergency or a "crash" procedure in 97 percent of the preventable cases, often the result of failed use of mid or high forceps or of family pressure (20 percent) to have a "natural delivery." Early discussions with the family and consultations with colleagues before or early in labor may avoid undue delays.

4. Transfers of more than 50 percent of the neonates in the preventable group to a neonatal intensive care unit suggest that careful evaluation of a mother's risk factors and assessment of a hospital's capabilities be done before or early in labor.

5. Family pressures that prevent or interfere with sound medical practice require early detailed discussions with all concerned parties and with colleague consultants and proper notation of such in the medical records.

6. Inadequate diagnostic criteria in a neonate include the failure to carefully chart meconium staining – an important time-related event in labor-head-chest circumferences, organomegaly and other stigmata of congenital infections or malformations.

7. "Birth asphyxia" or "perinatal anoxia" may be the only diagnosis in the absence of evidence of a careful work-up to consider alternative causes. This should include a review of the maternal medical history and pregnancy record, the use of ultrasound, TORCH titers, immunoglobulin M values, cultures and other diagnostic criteria to establish an etiologic diagnosis that may be related to congenital or familial factors. These conditions may be associated with a higher frequency of abnormal labors and deliveries than in normal infants.

8. The "late onset" of neurologic abnormalities, which occur months after the neonatal period, has often been attributed to either "birth injury" or "perinatal anoxia" without evidence of

carefully reviewing all of the records of the pregnancy, labor, and delivery relating to preventable events at birth. A complete family and genetic history and a thorough investigation of such post-neonatal events as infections or trauma appear indicated before a final diagnosis. Thus, both prenatal and postnatal events may be implicated in the increasing number of alleged neonatal "brain damage" claims. Preventable and non-preventable causes require precise, recorded documentation in order to institute measures to reduce the frequency of neurologic damage and unwarranted claims.

While clearly recognizing the limitations of a retrospective study, the records reviewed, the data recorded and analyzed and the implications of the results strongly support the concept of additional studies of this type. Finally, a structured, detailed record that includes a family history, a genetic history and specific details related to a mother's prior medical history, previous and current pregnancies, labor and deliveries is recommended for all hospitals and should be used in assessing any claim of neonatal "brain damage" attributed to alleged negligence.

With this material in hand, the advisory group turned to the question of how to use the data effectively. All of us had seen far too many valuable studies gathering dust on a shelf after being distributed. It was determined that to get necessary exposure of the report and motivate appropriate action it was important to broaden the base of involvement in the process to include a more diverse group, with strong participation by nursing, hospital administration, and even a strictly limited number of healthcare lawyers who had a reputation for problem-solving. Further, the entire substance of the original report should be put up for total review and reconstruction into a dynamic statewide course of action.

The advisory group then formally requested the California Hospital Association and the California Medical Association to sponsor a statewide conference on the subject of neonatal brain injury prevention. In addition to the Truck Insurance Exchange, the principal insurer for hospitals, each of the major physician liability carriers was asked to join in sponsorship, not only to obtain financial support but, more importantly, to assure their ultimate support of the recommendations coming out of the conference and to use their educational resources effectively.

In this regard, we anticipated the insurance carriers might be reluctant to support recommendations that might be interpreted as setting standards that would create potential additional grounds for professional liability in this highly sensitive and expensive liability area. This is always a friction point that must be faced in any effective injury prevention program. Historically, the physicians in California have been willing to accept this risk in supporting effective injury prevention activities, even though the selected approach must be carefully structured and the potential risks minimized. This requires a careful configuration of the language used. All but one of the carriers affirmatively responded.

With the appropriate support and funding assured, the advisory committee was expanded and the process of designing the conference content and strategy began. The determination was made that participation should be made by individual invitation, not to organizations, and that a three-day conference should be scheduled at a nice resort in Palm Springs. Although the participants would not be compensated, their expenses would be paid, including those of their spouse (this was in 1985). The conference was scheduled for a Thursday through mid-afternoon on Saturday so participants could stay over if they desired. We have found that this encourages full-time participation to the end. Nearly 100 persons were invited and 60 attended all sessions.

Each invitee was required to participate in one of seven workshops—each with its own chairperson plus a staff person from the medical or hospital association, who was responsible for preparing advance materials, an agenda, and a preliminary report for consideration by the work-shop participants. This advance preparation became a critical factor in the effectiveness of the workshop sessions. The seven workshops were designated as (1) Regionalization/Referrals, (2) Documentation and Diagnosis, (3) Intrapartum Fetal Evaluation and Use of Forceps, (4) Emergency Delivery, (5) Resuscitation, (6) Post Dates, and (7) Quality Assurance.

The workshops devoted approximately nine hours to the assigned area and some worked on into the night. Great emphasis was placed on the feasibility of each recommendation with appropriate concern for the legal implications of establishing potentially unrealistic standards of care. However, the thrust of all the working groups was that the importance of effective prevention assumed the need for some risk by healthcare providers. It should be noted that in 1985 the concept of the use of guidelines or parameters in medical practice was not widely accepted. In the last several years acceptance of guidelines has developed because of the actions by the American Medical Association and many of the specialty societies in developing parameters of care.

This issue required extensive writing and rewriting of some of the more controversial recommendations. Consideration had to be given to the fact that the report would be circulated to all hospitals in the spectrum, from the small rural hospital to the large teaching institutions. It was recognized that with the regionalization and networking implicit in the adopted approach, all potential resources should be considered and included.

The sections completed their work by the second evening and their material was presented to the general conference for a full-day session on the third day. Thus all 60 of the participants were fully involved in the final draft report. It was determined that in order to achieve effective understanding and implementation of the substance of the report, it would be necessary to repeat the process in two additional conferences, one in San Francisco and one in Los Angeles, by inviting a larger group to attend. These were one-day conferences that broke down into the same section pattern as the Palm Springs Conference and again acted on the total report.

Although no changes of substance were made at this step, the involvement of this larger group of individuals was a most effective tool in focusing interest in the process and the material. As a result, major progress in implementation was achieved before the final report was published. The last step before publication was formal approval by the governing bodies of both the medical association and the hospital association. Because of the unique nature of the project, neither of these approvals was routine.

Ten thousand copies of the report were printed and circulated to every hospital, their chiefs of staff, affected department heads and all obstetricians. The physician and hospital insurance carriers used the report as a basis for continued evaluation programs and review of actual procedures in hospitals and physician offices. One major physician carrier, Medical Insurance Exchange of California, as a condition for underwriting obstetrician coverage either on initial coverage or renewal, now requires that the insured certify in writing familiarity with the American College of Obstetricians and Gynecologists standards, a basic necessity for proper natal care. This action was significant because great reliance was placed on the practice recommendations of ACOG where applicable.

It should be noted that during the process outlined above, Truck Insurance Exchange continued to monitor reported infant brain damage cases and that the total number reviewed increased from 250 to 500. This process was watched carefully to see if the data would require any change in the recommendations, but the consequence was continued confirmation of the original conclusions. The database on risk factors was substantiated in part by a prior study in the Netherlands where there is no medical malpractice problem that could skew the data.

At a time when birth injury claims were dramatically increasing elsewhere in the United States, as exemplified by the drastic steps taken in such states as Virginia and Florida where no-fault systems of questionable design and results were implemented by the state legislature, the pattern of claims relating to infant brain damage in California showed dramatic improvement. The 1990 National Study by ACOG for 1989 data reported that the medical malpractice premiums for obstetricians for Region IX, which is limited to California, were the lowest of any of the ten regions in the country.

In considering the following data, a distinction must be made between claims, which may or may not lead to a paid loss, and paid losses – both as to number paid and the amount of indemnity paid. The Truck Insurance Exchange, the principal hospital carrier, reported that the number of newborn brain damage claims it received in California increased from 46 in 1983 to 75 in 1984, then jumped to 104 in 1985 and in 1986, but dropped to 72 in 1987, 63 in 1988, 66 in 1989, and 60 in 1990.

In its annual report for 1987 Medical Underwriters of California, the carrier that initiated the certificate of knowledge of ACOG standards as a condition of insurance or renewal by obstetricians, referred to above, reported that:

> A welcome decline in the number of birth injury cases resolved in 1987 led to a reduction in the percentage of total indemnity represented by this category from 58 percent in 1986 to 38 percent. Average indemnity to settle the nine birth injury cases reported in 1987 was $2,121,914, up ten percent from 1986, 17.4 percent from 1985, and 96 percent from 1984. Although only nine birth injury cases were reported in 1987, less than in any year since 1981, their indemnity costs still represented 37.8 percent of total indemnity for all 89 cases.
>
> Of the nine cases, six occurred in Southern California and three in Northern California. Five were resolved through structured settlements, one through a cash settlement and three by verdicts.

The same carrier in its 1990 study reported the number of cases for which it paid indemnity in excess of $50,000 for OB/GYN specialists dropped from 28 in 1986 to 14 in 1990. Of even greater importance was the finding that in 1986 the major birth injury cases represented 24.7 percent of the total of all major cases for which the carrier paid indemnity and 57.9 percent of the total indemnity for all major cases, but by 1990 the total number of major birth injury cases had been reduced to 7.1 percent of the total number of all major cases and 23.4 percent of the total indemnity paid. In its editorial comment on these figures the Medical Underwriters of California report states:

> Birth injury cases numbered eight in 1990, nearly unchanged since 1987 when they first receded from the higher levels of 1984 (13), 1985 (13) and 1986 (22). Their present value indemnity was $21 million, the highest since 1986. It took an average of only 54 months to resolve them, 17 months less than 1989's average. Only three birth injury cases were tried; the rest settled fairly quickly, perhaps indicating that both sides have sufficient experience in litigating this kind of case, establishing quickly whether liability exists and finding ways to settle when it does.

Without these results, there is a serious question as to whether the practice of obstetrics would be insurable in the marketplace in California. Of even greater importance to all of the participants in this project is the number of newborns who were saved from serious injury, even though the number of high-risk births increased materially with the advent of neonatal intensive care units and other innovations that saved the lives of an increasing number of endangered infants.

What we learned from this project is that it is possible to utilize liability claims data for the purpose of identifying potential high risks as well as to mobilize on a multi-disciplinary basis the various professions to analyze and create an injury prevention program that will make a major contribution to patient care. Furthermore, the positive impact on patients is far greater than shown by these figures. The Harvard Study indicates that only one out of 16 potential malpractice cases leads to a claim. Because of the high visibility of infant brain damage cases, we anticipate a higher claims ratio.

The other major lesson of this program is that by involving widespread representation of the affected professions in the development of the report, the positive impact manifested itself well before the report was in final form. The results of this project did not gather dust on a shelf.

The Foundation for Healthcare Quality in the state of Washington, a joint venture of the Washington hospital and medical associations and other interested groups, has received a major grant from the Hartford Foundation to develop a reliable, valid and clinically-relevant electronic database and information utility which will include data elements indicating quality of clinical obstetric care in Washington to be followed by a database concerning assessment of obstetric care. This project has the potential of developing positive assessment criteria based upon current practice patterns and resources that could update the work done by California Invitational II. Under the formidable title of "Statewide Obstetrics Review and Quality System" (StORQS), pronounced "Storks", its data is now available to the interested scholar.

15

Commission on Medical Malpractice

There was little activity at the national level about medical malpractice of hospitals and physicians until February, 1969, when the committee on government operations of the U.S. Senate directed the subcommittee on executive reorganization, which had been reviewing the federal role in healthcare problems of the nation, to investigate the apparent increase in medical malpractice litigation. The purpose of the inquiry, as stated by the chair of the subcommittee in a report that November was:

> We wanted to know what was behind the apparent rise in the number of suits. Was malpractice litigation an indication of the quality of care? Could the malpractice situation shed light on other healthcare problems? Was there a federal role in this area?

The report found: "Our preliminary research revealed a surprising lack of information. There were few statistics. There was no basic literature in the field." The subcommittee then requested suggestions from healthcare providers, insurance companies and the Department of Health, Education and Welfare, as it was then known.

My only involvement in this preliminary report was that the report reprinted in its entirety a two-part article I had authored for the March 16, 1961, issue of *Hospitals,* the official magazine of the American Hospital Association, entitled "Better Patient Care Through Group Liability Insurance." This spelled out in extensive detail how a state hospital association or the medical profession in a state could create a joint program to attack at the state level the problem of quality of care. As I now reread the article I find its detailed recommendations on the structure, philosophy and implementation of such a program are still valid. It was, of course, based upon the California Hospital Association group program developed in 1954, discussed elsewhere in this book.

In any event, this led to my being appointed by Elliot L. Richardson, Secretary of HEW in the Nixon Administration, to what was called the "Secretary's Commission on Medical Malpractice." Its "Statement of Formal Determination" set forth its purpose:

> The Commission will advise the Secretary with respect to the entire range of problems associated with professional liability (malpractice) claims against all categories of healthcare providers and institutions in both the Federal and private sectors, and will make recommendations as to the legislative, administrative and programmatic actions calculated to ameliorate the problems so identified.
>
> The Commission additionally will advise the Secretary with respect to the sources and availability of basic statistical information about malpractice and malpractice claims, both Federal and non-Federal, and will determine the feasibility, costs, and methodology of establishing a nationwide data gathering capability to enable the continuous monitoring of malpractice claims experience and study of malpractice related problems."

Creating the 21-member commission came from the president's health message of February 18, 1971. All members were from the private sector and represented healthcare providers and institutions, the legal profession, the insurance industry and the general public. The appointees were a high-powered crowd, including Charles A. Hoffman, M.D., president of the AMA, George W. Northrup, D.O., past president of the American Osteopathic Association and Richard M. Markus, LL.B. past president of the American Trial Lawyers Association, with other individuals of varied backgrounds.

The staff, led by Eli P. Bernzweig, executive director, with nine assistants had a six-member support staff. Most of the staff were on loan from interested federal departments and the commission was given a deadline until the end of 1972 to complete its task. It spent the first seven months holding public meetings at which any individual could appear without screening – one each in Los Angeles, Cincinnati, New Orleans, New York and Denver, with two in Washington, D.C. Generally these lasted two days over a weekend with sessions of up to nine hours. We heard 212 witnesses and the transcript of the hearings ran to 3,568 pages. Following these public hearings, the commission held a series of two- and three-day meetings in Washington for a total of 21 days' deliberation.

Although the staff was responsible for the development of proposed commission recommendations based upon the hearings and the commission discussions, the commission voted on, approved or modified more than 90 suggestions that covered the entire spectrum of healthcare, going from national health insurance to institutional licensure. In other words, anything that could be considered as having a remote connection to the quality of healthcare was included in its broad social policy sweep. There was something for everybody in the smörgåsbord of recommendations, which were either findings, recommendations or both.

What was missing was far more important than what was included, particularly as to what are now considered the prime approaches to the medical malpractice reform through a reform of the tort system. The recommendations that dealt with the existing tort system related to informed consent, *res ipsa loquitor,* statute of limitations, contingent fees, expert testimony, notice of intent to sue, and the elimination of *ad damnun* clauses. There were no recommendations, or even discussion, of such issues as a cap on judgments for pain and suffering, the use of periodic payments, the problems of joint and several liability. The matter of punitive damages, limits on contingent fees, and the collateral source rule were discussed only in the concept of national health insurance.

A large part of this lack of focus by the commission arose because results of the $1.5 million dollars in research grants were not received or placed in the hands of the commission in time for their contents to be considered prior to the drafting of the report. And a great disappointment for the commission members was that the office of the secretary of H.E.W. refused to extend the December 31, 1972, deadline for the life of the commission. After that date we were not allowed to meet and review as a group the report as prepared by our staff, but had to individually comment within a very short time frame.

Under the leadership of Dr. Hoffman from the AMA, an appeal was made to President Nixon's office requesting an extension of the commission's life. Commission members even offered to pay our own expenses for additional Washington, D.C. meetings if an extension were granted. It was reported back that H.R. Haldeman, Nixon's chief of staff, blocked the approach to the president so it failed. That was as close as we got to Watergate. The report itself was 146 pages long with an appendix of the research papers being an additional 850 pages. These research papers for the first time established a database on many aspects of medical practice, documenting various efforts at the state level to find resolutions.

One of the most important results of this publication was to encourage the National Association of Insurance Commissioners in 1975 – 1976 to initiate and publish an annual closed-claims study for the entire U.S. When this report came out in December 1975, for the first time it gave a nationwide perspective on medical malpractice claims and their disposition, providing detailed information on cost, severity and frequency of closed claims with breakdowns not only by specialty but also where the occurrences arose within the hospital. Unfortunately, it carried the burden of looking backwards over the eight years that the entire spectrum of claims developed from the actual occurrence to the final closing, and did not cover newly developing trends that would have shown current claims which had not been closed. This study continued for a number of years until it was abandoned for cost reasons.

Reflecting on the commission's worth, it is my viewpoint that it was a good start at calling attention to the developing problems but that it never got truly focused on the issue of tort reform. As a practical matter, the existence of an early warning system on potential liability issues still does not exist, although there is now the potential for developing a database through the work of the integrated medical groups and their relationship with the managed-care plans where the emphasis is on outcomes. Increasingly outcomes studies combined with protocols or "best practice" concepts should deal with the cost and quality of care.

Personally, I found the most important benefit from the long hours and weekend plane trips devoted to commission work was the opportunity to become thoroughly acquainted with Hap Hassard, the general counsel to the California Medical Association as well as many county medical societies in Northern California and their key physician medical malpractice insurance plans. Through this personal relationship, coupled with mutual confidence and shared commitment to resolution of problems between our constituents, we learned to work together in facing the common enemy – whether it be trial lawyers, the legislature or agitators within our own participants. The ability to call Hap any time and get sound advice on very sensitive matters served both physicians and hospitals constructively. It was to the benefit of physicians, hospitals and the public served that this unique relationship continued as Dave Willett, who succeeded Hap, and Chuck Forbes, on behalf of our firm, assumed a similar relationship.

There was no immediate action at the federal level as the result of the report. As a consequence the battle for medical malpractice tort reform continued to be fought out at the state level. There has recently been some activity at the federal level because of the fall-out of some specific tort reform provisions in the Hillary Clinton health reform proposal – which was aborted as a total project. Congress continues to consider specific legislative proposals on tort reform within the entire tort system as well as specific proposals on issues relating to product liability and medical malpractice, but so far we have had no positive resolutions on these matters.

16

Commission on Medical Liability

In the past two decades the American Bar Association has been peculiarly ineffective in providing any leadership in resolving the legal issues relating to medical malpractice. In substantial part this was the result of opposition of the plaintiff's bar to any reform, but there was also indifference by the defense bar to taking any leadership position on behalf of their physician and hospital clients.

One major exception to this pattern of indifference was an action by the House of Delegates of the ABA to establish "The American Bar Association Commission on Medical Professional Liability" at its annual meeting in 1975 with 15 members, mostly individuals with legal background, but it also included physicians, lawyers and public members. The chairperson, Lyman M. Tondel, Jr., was former president of the New York Bar Association. Among the participants were many leaders in the practice of law including two who were to run for the presidency of the ABA. I was appointed to the commission, apparently as past president of the American Society of Hospital Attorneys as well as because of my experience on the DHEW Secretary's Commission On Medical Malpractice. Another former member of the secretary's commission was included in this new commission, Richard M. Markus, past president of the American Trial Lawyers Association, who served until 1976 when he was appointed to a federal judgeship.

The commission members listed on the 1977 final report were: Lyman M. Tondel, Jr., New York (chair), past president, New York State Bar Association; former member of the ABA board of governors; and president of the Institute of Judicial Administration. Leonard S. Janofsky, Los Angeles (vice-chair), former president of both the National Conference of Bar Presidents and the California Bar Association. Betty Capps, Denver, director of the Nutrition Programs for the Elderly, Department of Social Services, State of Colorado and chair of the Home Economists in Human Services Professional Section, American Home Economics Association. Dr. James K. Cooper, Washington, D.C., Office of the Assistant Secretary of Health, U.S. Department of Health, Education and Welfare. Dr. John J. Coury, Jr., Port Huron, Michigan, former president, Michigan State Medical Society and member of the council on legislation and the board of trustees, American Medical Association. John C. Deacon, Jonesboro, Arkansas, former president, Arkansas Bar Association and Member of the special committee on medical malpractice and the executive committee of the Commissioners on Uniform State Laws. Dr. William F. Donaldson, Pittsburgh, immediate past president, American Academy of Orthopedic Surgeons. Everett L. Hollis, Chicago, former general counsel, Atomic Energy Commission. James E. Ludlam, Los Angeles, former president, American Society of Hospital Attorneys and counsel, California Hospital Association. Richard M. Markus, Cleveland, former president, Association of Trial Lawyers of America and adjunct professor at both Cleveland State University

Law School and Case Western Reserve University Law School. When Mr. Markus resigned in 1976 on becoming a judge of the Court of Common Pleas in Ohio, the Honorable John J. Sullivan of the Appellate Court, Fifth Division, in Chicago, was appointed to fill this vacancy. Other members were Lester L. Rawls, Salem, Oregon, chair of the committee on medical malpractice and chair of executive committee of the National Association of Insurance Commissioners; Lester F. Senger, Hartford, Connecticut, vice-president, industry affairs, Aetna Life and Casualty Co. and chair of the American Insurance Association special committee on medical malpractice; Donald B. Straus, New York, president, Research Institute of the American Arbitration Association and former president, American Arbitration Association; Jerry V. Walker, Houston, president, International Association of Insurance Counsel and member of the executive committee, Defense Research Institute; and Judge Joseph Weintraub, Orange, New Jersey, former chief justice of the State of New Jersey.

This was a hard-working group which held 17 full commission meetings and 40 subcommittee meetings. I chaired Subcommittee II dealing with improving the tort system and served on the subcommittees on arbitration/panels, and prevention. The timing of this study had a major impact on the focus of the report because the medical malpractice insurance crisis was bubbling in various states, emphasizing the need for some action.

Because of the time pressure intensified by outside forces over the issue of medical practice insurance costs, the commission published and forwarded an interim report to the House of Delegates of the American Bar in August 1976. In addition to furnishing a comprehensive analysis of the problem, the interim report provided certain specific recommendations for approval of the House of Delegates, most of which were approved. Those approved were:

1. That absolute immunity from civil liability should be conferred on members of a medical discipline board, including

any officially established state body, medical society or hospital review committee responsible for investigating the professional conduct of physicians in order to determine whether disciplinary sanction should be established either as a part of licensure or as a part of the law requiring disciplinary actions at the hospital level. This followed the pattern of a series of statutes adopted in California in the 1960s which had been most successful. As a part of this recommendation the proceedings of such disciplinary boards or committees should be immune from discovery, and, in addition, to assure frank and open participation, no person attending a meeting of such a board could testify as to what occurred at the meeting.

2. In response to the great concern of the medical profession relating to the traditional civil court process, the commission recommended that all states adopt uniform laws authorizing the arbitration of medical malpractice disputes; also, that while the arbitration agreement should be on a voluntary basis, any decision should be final and binding once entered into. No recommendation was made at that time as to whether the arbitration agreement could be entered into before the malpractice occurrence. This was a controversial issue and action was postponed to the final report.

3. The commission report brought to the forefront the fact that at this point in time, in many parts of the country, medical malpractice insurers were withdrawing from the market and no malpractice insurance was available.

4. The commission recommended that all states should adopt legislation permitting the establishment of joint underwriting associations of some type to assure the availability of medical malpractice insurance on a temporary basis.

5. Although the preliminary report discussed certain proposed tort law changes, it recommended that this inclusion in the report was solely to encourage discussion of these items, and that the final recommendations should be brought back to the House of Delegates for action at a future date.

The specific tort reforms referred to dealt with the following issues: 1) informed consent, 2) statute of limitations, 3) notice of intent to sue, 4) access to medical records, 5) panels and experts, 5) advance payments, 7) *ad damnum* clauses, 8) exchange of expert reports, 9) guarantee of results, 10) *res ipsa loquitur*, 11) itemized

Health Policy – The Hard Way

verdicts, 12) ceiling on awards, 13) collateral source rule, 14) non-taxable status of awards, 15) prejudgment interest; 16) punitive damages, 17) periodic payments, and 18) contingent fees. The report included an analysis of each of these proposals.

After considerable additional work the commission published its final document October 31, 1977, pointing out that when the commission was organized in 1975 the healthcare community was in the midst of the medical malpractice crisis. As the report states, "Now, a little more than two years later, the medical malpractice crisis seems to have abated, and much of the attention has shifted to products liability, legal malpractice and municipal liability."

The final statement analyzed the causes of the medical malpractice crisis and the steps taken to assure the continued availability of medical professional liability insurance as well as the activities at the state level that stabilized the insurance market. It described the set of system goals which the commission adopted to guide its work product:

1. Encourage the prompt availability of remedial medical services to injured persons;
2. Compensate all persons deemed compensable under the mechanism;
3. Pay a victim of a compensable medical incident at least the net economic loss occasioned by the incident;
4. Provide for the prompt resolution of claims;
5. Charge a minimum of administrative costs (including attorneys' fees) and make a maximum amount available for the injured person;
6. Insure maximum predictability of outcome as an aid to planning by healthcare providers and insurers;
7. Discourage the bringing of baseless or contrived claims and provide for their prompt elimination if brought;
8. Contribute to the prevention of malpractice incidents by introducing incentives for improving healthcare and for improving the supervision and discipline of healthcare personnel;
9. Distribute losses, through insurance or otherwise, in a way which does not leave an unfair burden on any one segment of the healthcare system; and

10. Disrupt to the least possible degree the relationships of trust and confidence between healthcare providers and patients.

The report then dealt with such issues as patients' rights and responsibilities, patient safety programs, medical discipline, dispute resolution with emphasis on the use of arbitration, pretrial review panels, small claims, special urban malpractice courts, ending up with a comprehensive review of tort laws and procedural issues including lawyers' professional responsibility.

The role of the liability insurance industry was reviewed with the conclusion that the insurance industry had its own problems with the subject but did not appear to have ripped off the healthcare providers. It also dealt with various innovative alternatives to solve the problem of availability of insurance, including the use of a system of compensating patient injuries pursuant to a set of defined compensable events on a quasi-workers-compensation approach which the commission believed was worthy of experimentation if coupled with further data collection and research.

The report then concluded with its most controversial proposed twelve tort law and procedure recommendations and the reasons for their support. These were:

1. *Notice of Intent to Sue,* which would require the plaintiff to give reasonable (90 to 180 days) written notice of intention to sue to each prospective defendant, with sanctions on the attorney for failure to provide the notice.

This was one of my pets that I strongly supported in the California 1975 MICRA legislation. The purpose of the proposal was to establish a potential process for resolution of claims prior to the trauma of filing a suit and thereby lessen the animosity between the parties. My experience had been that the impact, particularly upon a physician, of being served by a marshal or other process-server with a cold-blooded complaint was emotionally devastating to the doctor who might not have even known there was a complaint by the patient. Lawyers just did not appreciate what the process did to the physician-patient relationship or the attitude of the medical profession toward the role of the plaintiff attorney.

This was one lesson that had come through loud and clear at the public hearings held by the secretary's commission. It was to be hoped that physicians' defense counsel and insurance company could get at the merits of the matter at an early date, possibly to resolve the matter before a court record was established as a permanent blot on the record of the physician or hospital. It would also give time to initiate an arbitration or mediation process.

2. *Informed Consent.* The commission recommended that a cause of action for lack of informed consent should not be treated as an action for battery, but rather as an action for negligence unless there was an allegation of intent to harm or deceive the patient. This was important because a battery or fraud allegation could be the basis for a punitive damage action or in any event an inflammatory charge for the jury to consider. There was evidence of abuse by plaintiff attorneys using such allegations to intimidate physicians into making extraordinary settlement offers. Also, in many states an intentional tort such as battery or fraud was not insurable, so the defendant would also be receiving a notice from his insurance carrier that the carrier was reserving the right to deny coverage and defense costs. The report emphasized the importance of the informed consent process to the patient. However, it pointed out that the grounds for liability should be based on the failure of the physician to explain the risks as well as the alternatives to the proposed procedure and that liability should be based on expert testimony to the effect that a reasonable patient who had been adequately informed would not have consented to the procedure or treatment.

3. *Statute of Limitations.* Because of the importance of an effective statute of limitations and the need to provide a balance between the rights of the patients, on the one hand, and that of the defendant healthcare providers on the other, the commission worked out a fairly complete series of compromises in an attempt to be fair to both sides.

The proposed statute is as follows:

(a) An action for medical malpractice should commence within two years from the time the incident which gave rise to the action occurred or within one year from the time the existence of an actionable injury is discovered or in the exercise of reasonable care should have been discovered, whichever is longer. Except for cases involving a foreign object or fraudulent concealment, no action should be brought more than eight years after the occurrence of the incident which gave rise to the injury.

(b) Where a foreign object has been left in the body, a patient should have one year after the object is discovered in which to bring an action.

(c) Where fraudulent concealment of material facts by a healthcare provider has prevented the discovery of the injury or the alleged negligence, the patient should have one year after discovering that an actionable injury exists in which to bring suit.

(d) The statute of limitations should be tolled during continuous treatment by the same healthcare provider for the same condition or for complications arising from original treatment.

(e) The statute of limitations should apply equally to adults and minors alike except that a minor's representative should have until the minor's eighth birthday to commence a suit, regardless of how many years earlier the cause of action accrued.

The most controversial provision was one that stated that the statute should apply equally to adults and minors, although the minor's representative would have until the minor's eighth birthday to commence the suit. This concept was developed during a time when there was a major increase in the number and severity of actions for birth injuries and at the time minority went to age 21, not 18 as it is now.

Unless such a special limit was adopted, minors in most states would have until their 23rd birthday to bring suit. A malpractice insurer would have no way of anticipating its future liability for birth injuries and, as a result, might either withdraw from the market entirely or, of necessity, substantially increase premiums to obstetricians as well as general practice doctors who delivered babies. It was clearly evident that a substantial number of doctors, particularly in the rural areas, were totally withdrawing from the

Health Policy – The Hard Way

practice of delivering babies or acting as pediatricians at or immediately following a birth because of cost or unavailability of liability insurance for this practice.

The commission took the viewpoint expressed by the plaintiff attorneys that the patient must not only discover the injury but also must be aware of facts which suggest that the injury may have been the result of negligence. The inclusion of a continuous treatment tolling provision was also important in encouraging the patient to seek recourse through remedial care furnished by the potential defendant healthcare provider rather than through the courts. This concept was based upon the experience of some of the early managed-care plans, such as Kaiser Permanente, finding that they could maintain the physician-patient relationship and resolve the patient's grievance internally – an approach that is even more important now with the rapid shift to managed care.

4. *Guarantee of Results.* This proviso recommended that a healthcare provider should not be held liable for promising a particular outcome unless such guarantee was in writing and signed by the party charged. This was to deal not only with the ambiguity of an oral guarantee but also with the apparent abuse of claiming oral guarantees.

5. *Res Ipsa Loquitur.* The commission adopted with modifications the recommendation of the American Medical Association as follows: No liability for personal injury or death shall be imposed against any provider of medical care based on alleged negligence in the performance of such care unless expert medical testimony is presented as to the alleged deviation from the accepted standard of care in the specific circumstances of the case and as to the causation of the alleged personal injury or death, except that such expert medical testimony shall not be required and a [rebuttable] *permissible* inference that the personal injury or death was caused by negligence shall arise where evidence is presented that the personal injury or death occurred in any one or more of the following circumstances; (1) A foreign [substance] *object* other than medication or a prosthetic device was unintentionally left within the body of a patient following surgery, (2) an explosion or fire originating in a substance used in treatment

occurred in the course of treatment, (3) an unintended burn caused by heat, radiation or chemicals was suffered in the course of medical care, [(4) an injury was suffered during the course of treatment to a part of the body not directly involved in such treatment or proximate thereto,] or [5](4) a surgical procedure was performed on the wrong patient or the wrong organ, limb or part of a patient's body.

6. *Ceiling on Awards.* On this, the most controversial issue before the commission, the commission recommended there be no dollar limit on recoverable damages for economic loss by the patient. On the issue of noneconomic loss the commission took no position on whether it was appropriate to place a ceiling, thus leaving this highly controversial issue open.

This was a major concession to the plaintiffs' bar in the forlorn hope that it might encourage that group to take a more positive approach to the other recommendations of the commission. As will be seen later, that was a futile hope.

7. *Collateral Source Rule.* In my judgment the most important recommendation of the commission dealt with the collateral source rule and provided: Recovery of damages should be reduced by collateral source payments received by the plaintiff as the result of government, employment-related, individually purchased and gratuitously conferred benefits. (The commission did not take a position on whether any forms of life insurance benefits should be offset.) The amounts to be set off should be deducted by the judge from the jury's assessment of damages against the defendant. Subrogation should not be allowed to any collateral source for medical benefits thus set off. (The commission did not take any position on subrogation as to wage and disability payments.)

As noted, the set off of the collateral source payments was mandated as a matter of law and not left to the jury's discretion or even knowledge. The commission concluded that the provision of insurance coverage for injuries is handled much more efficiently through the healthcare insurance system rather than the tort system, and the potential windfall to the plaintiff by double or multiple recovery from collateral sources was both costly and without justification.

In the committee discussions it was pointed out there was a clear precedent for this approach in the field of fire insurance where by law in nearly all states an owner of an insured fire loss structure could not recover more than the total loss regardless of how many insurance policies might be in effect. This was reportedly to deal with the problem of farmers or office building owners torching their own property to make a substantial financial killing in times of depression.

There is also the similar problem faced by health insurers when a multiplicity of group insurance policies are available should both the husband and wife be employed with health insurance benefits. One of my partners said many years ago, before the health insurance companies rewrote their policies to coördinate the benefits to avoid multiple coverage beyond the actual economic loss to the insureds, "I can't afford to leave the hospital with all those benefit checks coming in."

When we in California attempted to identify for discovery purposes all of the possible multiple recovery sources, the list was four pages long. The commission recommendations also protected the plaintiff patient from the recovery by subrogation of any of the collateral sources. Later in this book a discussion of the collateral source rule under the California MICRA statute will describe a somewhat different approach to the collateral source rule reform.

    8. *Maintain Nontaxable Status of Awards.* This was a new issue raised because recoveries by a plaintiff for personal injury are not subject to income tax and, in effect, damages recovered for loss of income are converted from taxable income to nontaxable income. Also this provision encouraged the use of periodic payments in lieu of lump sum awards, as an income tax is assessed against the income that plaintiff receives from investing a lump sum award, but the installments under a periodic payment are not taxable.

9. *Punitive Damages.* Although there were not many reported attempts to collect punitive damages in medical malpractice
cases back then, the commission observed that the pattern and
potential abuse of such claims was a real threat and should be
handled with the following recommendation: Punitive damages
should not be allowed in medical malpractice cases. Rather, the
medical discipline system, hospital licensure statutes and the
criminal justice system should be relied on for such punitive
action against an offending physician as may be justified.

The commission's discussion pointed out the possible double
jeopardy of the physician from criminal or disciplinary action by
the state or by the hospital. Also a demand for punitive damages
is counter-productive in that it heightens the adversary nature of
medical malpractice litigation and needlessly complicates settlement
negotiations. The commission did not point out that in most states
punitive damages are not insurable, so the defendant must personally pay for such recovery, thus creating a conflict between the
defendant and his insurance carrier on the matter of settlements.
A lump-sum settlement with blanket releases negotiated by the
insurance carrier can automatically wipe out any punitive damage
recovery against the insured physician; this motivates the defendant physician or hospital to demand that their insurance company
settle within policy limits. This also creates problems for defense
counsel assigned by the carrier to defend the doctor: to whom
should their loyalties go – the carrier or the doctor?

10. *Periodic Payments.* One of the most innovative recommendations made by the commission related to the support of
the concept of periodic payments or structured awards, however
they may be described. The recommendation was: Legislation
should be enacted in all states to permit the payment of future
damages in periodic installments.

At the time this recommendation was made there was little
experience with this approach except for a start-up program in
California, so the action of the commission was solely one of con-

cept. However, the underlying theory was that such an award could not only be in the best interest of the injured party by being designed as need-based, but also had the potential of reducing the cost to the defendant funding the award. In actual practice, as will be discussed when we come to MICRA, the use of the procedure has become quite sophisticated and useful for all parties.

Although the plaintiff's bar has challenged the limitation of the award to the life of the plaintiff, they have failed to recognize that the life of the plaintiff may well exceed the funding of a lump-sum award; thus the trade-off is the guarantee for life of the annuity as a protection from premature exhaustion of the award on the one hand, or a windfall to heirs or other third parties on the other. The actual result has been that where experienced attorneys are involved in a settlement negotiation, a truly constructive innovative award can be designed. The indirect benefit has been greater than the direct benefit in actual trial results.

11. *Contingent Fees*. Although the commission supported the concept of the continuation of the use of contingent fees, the commission recommended, in a very terse statement: A decreasing maximum schedule for contingent fees should be set by court order, provided that such schedule should not be so restrictive, particularly with respect to small to moderate recoveries, that it hampers the ability of injured patients to obtain legal representation.

In addition the commission stated: "Because the regulation of legal practice is regarded almost universally as the responsibility of the judicial branch of government, it is preferable that any regulation of contingent fees be accomplished by court order rather than legislative enactment." It also pointed out that fees should be related more to actual attorney work and less to the fortuity of the defendant's economic status and degree of injury of the plaintiff.

12. *Locality Rule and Expert Witnesses*. At the time of the report there was much litigation over the continuation of the

locality rule as well as to the difference in the standard of care by a specialist as contrasted with a general practitioner. The commission recommended:

(a) A physician who presents himself to the public as a specialist (whether or not certified in that specialty), should be judged by national standards applicable to that specialty. A general practitioner or a family practice specialist (even though certified as) should be judged by the standards of such physicians in the same or similar locality.

(b) To be competent to testify for or against a defendant, the witness should be a physician who is actively practicing the same field or specialty as the defendant was practicing in at the time of the incident, or in a field or specialty which is closely related thereto.

The report includes an extended discussion of the issue and ends up with an additional recommendation:

In addition, in order to assure that the necessary clinical perspective is present, and that the abuses caused by those who do little else but testify in malpractice cases are curbed, the commission recommends that only active clinicians in the applicable specialty be allowed to testify.

❦ Response of the American Trial Lawyers Association

In its response to both the interim report and the final report the ATLA stated it had no objection to the following eight recommendations:

- Notice of Intent to Sue
- Access to Medical Records
- Panels of Experts
- Advance Payments
- *Ad Damnum* Clause
- Exchange of Expert Reports
- Itemized Verdicts
- Pre-judgment Interest

As to the remaining recommendations, it did not concur: 1) On informed consents, it agreed on the concept that lack of informed consent was a negligence liability rather than assault and battery unless there had been no consent whatsoever by the patient, in which case it may be treated as assault and battery. The duty to disclose for informed consent purposes should be based on the needs of the patient rather than the custom of the medical profession, so the legal standard should be that of the particular patient's understanding, given a particular mental and psychological makeup. 2) On statute of limitations, objection was made to the absolute limit of eight years for minors. 3) In addition, objections were made to the recommendations as to guarantee of results, *res ipsa loquitur,* collateral source rule, nontaxable status of awards, punitive damages, periodic payments and contingent fees.

On the matter of ceiling on awards, the CTLA and the ATLA objected to the failure of the commission to recommend against such a ceiling.

❦ *Action by the House of Delegates*

In accordance with ABA procedure, the report was circulated to the ABA membership with a cover letter from Lyman Tondel, chair, giving notice that if any member desired any recommendation to be considered by the House of Delegates at its February 1978 annual meeting in New Orleans, it should do so in writing by January 1, 1978.

Because of this, formal request was made for consideration of the commission proposals on 1) statute of limitations on minors' claims, 2) the collateral source rule, 3) jury instructions as to the nontaxable status of portions of verdicts in medical negligence cases, 4) punitive damages, and 5) periodic payment of verdicts.

In anticipation of this result, the commission was required to appoint a member to present these special recommendations to the full House of Delegates which would, in turn, act upon each one, to accept, reject or modify. At a special meeting of the commission the selection of the representative was up for consideration. For some reason then unknown to me neither the chair nor any of the other members seemed enthusiastic about taking the job, so after some flattering remarks about my special knowledge of the subject based upon what had been happening in California I was unanimously selected for the role.

After it was all over I fully understood the lack of volunteers.

In any event, I went to New Orleans to appear at a special order of business for the House of Delegates in the banquet room of the convention center. Several hundred delegates were seated in the center of the room grouped by states. The officers and trustees were on a raised dais in the front of the room with a standing mike in front of the officers for any person addressing the officers and trustees plus five or six mikes located throughout the hall for any member who wished to be heard. I was ushered into a special section on the left of the room and placed in the front row to be available when called. A couple members of the commission came up and joined me but the rest were not in sight.

Around eleven that morning the matter was called and I approached the speaker's mike. There was considerable activity in the room as many groups clustered and conferred. Almost immediately there were individuals lined up at all of the member mikes. I presented the first of the five commission recommendations scheduled on the statute of limitations, first reading the formal language of the commission statement, then giving a brief background argument in favor of its adoption.

This was followed by a deluge as the presiding officer called upon the individuals at the various mikes. Each one was well prepared with a brief statement of opposition upon the part of their own state delegation, including at least one horror story. No one present spoke in support of our recommendation, so the presiding officer soon cut off discussion and called for an oral vote. There were some favorable voices, but the OPPOSITION was overwhelming and the spread was so great there was no need to request a count of hands or a roll call. The same process was followed for the other four recommendations that were reviewed. I have had my share of experiences in being clobbered by legislative committees, but never anything like this.

It was obvious the ATLA had worked over each state delegation lining up the votes. Besides, no organization was working to support our program. As a result all five of the tort reforms that had substance, including the repeal of the collateral source rule, the limit on contingency fees, punitive damages, periodic payments and statute of limitations, went down in flames. I also figured out why none of the old-timers on the commission had volunteered to make the presentation and why I was chosen to be the sacrificial lamb as my first experience in bar association politics.

Although no specific positive results can be identified from the work of the commission, it did, for the first time, zero in on tort reform as providing the greatest relief to healthcare providers from the rapid increases in the cost of malpractice liability insurance. Besides, the concentration and analysis of the various tort reform proposals were educational to individuals such as myself who were fighting the battle at the state legislative level. Certainly the quality of the legislative activity at the state level was substantially improved by this exercise.

In conclusion, it became clear the ATLA could and would bottle up any attempt by the American Bar Association to take a responsible leadership role in attacking the problem. Further, any immediate hope for action at the federal level was definitely deferred for an extended period of time.

17

The Medical Injury Compensation Reform Act of 1975 (MICRA)

S tarting in 1971 there was a nationwide explosive surge in the number of malpractice claims made against hospitals and physicians, particularly in California and other major urban states. From 1970 through 1974 the claims frequency doubled even though there was no identifiable cause for this increase. There was every indication the trend would continue; worse, there was a doubling in the cost per resolved claim for this period which compounded the result. This meant it would require a premium of four times what was charged in 1970 to cover the losses in 1974. With the trend continuing premium cost could double and quadruple again in a few short years. From the insurance company's viewpoint, they had to collect premiums in the current year to cover cases not settled immediately that would mature over a period of at least five years and be based upon the cost of the claim when paid, not when it occurred.

Health Policy – The Hard Way

The crisis of 1975 that led to passage of the Medical Injury Compensation Act (MICRA) in California was driven by the cost increases and the reduced availability of medical malpractice insurance. Primarily this was an issue for the physician community whose annual malpractice premiums totalled three times those of hospitals. However, it was equally true that the physicians' problems quickly became the hospitals' as physicians were either forced out of California, withdrew from practice or went uninsured to protest their individual difficulty with increased premium costs or termination of coverage.

An understanding of the structure of the insurance market for both physicians and hospitals is necessary to follow the saga of the years since 1970. Malpractice insurance for physicians was not made available on a statewide basis by the California Medical Association but was provided as a service of the county medical societies, each having its own sponsored plan with a chosen carrier under a separate contract. A half dozen commercial insurance companies competed for these plans and other commercial carriers were active in the market for insuring individual physicians.

Under this pattern of multiple competing carriers, no central control or responsibility existed at the state level to assure the availability of insurance for the medical profession. Furthermore, the county societies occasionally changed carriers. Thus in 1970 the Los Angeles County Medical Association switched from the Nettleship Company program to Hartford and again in 1974 to Travelers because of the Nettleship's request for a substantial premium increase. Both Hartford and then Travelers were willing to take the risk with a negotiated premium for the first year and an agreement they would not increase premiums by more than ten percent in each of the following two years. With the rapid increase in frequency and severity of claims against doctors the premiums proved totally inadequate. Then these carriers announced that when their contracts ran out they would either substantially increase their rates or withdraw from the market. This same story was told throughout the state.

As a result, the California Assembly created a select committee on medical malpractice in 1972 with Henry A. Waxman as chair. Of enormous significance was their choosing attorney Fred J. Hiestand as consultant to the committee. As will be seen, he became one of the most critical players in the entire process leading to the eventual design, passage and implementation of the Medical Injury Compensation Reform Act, which continues to the present.

Fred is a unique person with many special qualifications which made him critical to the ultimate success of the MICRA project. Growing up in the rough-and-tumble politics of the East Bay, he was a dedicated liberal deeply committed to causes and projects for the benefit of the underprivileged and racial minorities. He was also thoroughly familiar with the inner workings of the Legislature and the governor's office at a time when liberal Democrats were in power, with majorities in both branches of the Legislature as well as having Jerry Brown as governor.

Fortunately, in my early lawyer years I was involved in many people-oriented community projects, serving as board president for the Children's Bureau of Los Angeles, chair of the children's division of the Los Angeles Welfare Planning Council, then chair of the council itself, chair of the Los Angeles Adoption Committee and member of the state executive committee that broke the black market in adoptions. I was chair of the Welfare Planning Council at the time of the first Watts riots and so was well attuned and sympathetic to Fred's causes. We were always able to understand each other in this new cause of malpractice tort reform.

The select committee held its first public meeting in Los Angeles in November of 1973, followed the next month by a smaller meeting in San Francisco. These hearings were well attended and gave the doctors, hospitals and their representatives an opportunity to expose the growing problem of medical malpractice costs and,

166   Health Policy – The Hard Way

in turn, a chance for the California Trial Lawyers Association to blame it all on the insurance companies as well as the quality-of-care problems of both physicians and hospitals.

There was little proposed in the way of tort reform, although in my testimony I discussed the matters of duplicate cost recovery by plaintiffs under the collateral-source rule. That rule permitted the injured patient to make multiple recovery for the same medical care costs from both the health insurers and the malpractice defendants. I pointed out the far greater efficiency of the health insurance system compared to the tort system in compensating for the healthcare costs of injured parties.

Not until the 1974 hearing of the select committee in Los Angeles and the 1975 hearing in Sacramento did witnesses begin to delineate specific tort reform proposals. The first came from Assemblyperson Alister McAlister who had introduced legislation authorizing the insurance commission to create a joint underwriting association to set the rates and underwriting requirements. The association would set rates on a self-supporting basis by assessment against all admitted liability carriers as well as the insured doctors. In other words, this would deal with the availability of coverage but would not have a direct impact on the cost through any reform of the underlying tort system.

Dr. Stanley Moore, president of CMA, appeared with Howard Hassard, legal counsel for CMA and Jack Curley, director of member services. They proposed that for the short term a consortium of carriers be created to pool the risk and assure availability of insurance. For the long term they recommended that tort law be revised so as to create a statute of limitation based on the date of injury rather than the date of discovery, establishing court administered trusts for longevity awards, requiring that juries be informed regarding a plaintiff's collateral sources of injury compensation, the nontaxable status of awards and the remarriage of a plaintiff in a wrongful death action. They also proposed contingent fees be limited to a graduated scale pattern similar to that established in New Jersey, and requirement of a 60-day notice of intent to sue.

Monsignor Timothy O'Brien, as chair of the CHA insurance committee, proposed essentially the same items as did Dr. Moore, but also noted the dilemmas hospitals faced if their medical staff were not insured, because the hospitals were mandating that a member of the medical staff have insurance as a condition of membership as authorized by the 1974 legislation. He emphasized that the physician crisis could quickly become a hospital crisis. The California Association of Neurological Surgeons sent Mr. Charles O'Brien who made a strong plea for legislative support of the use of arbitration to resolve medical malpractice claims, this despite opposition to the process by various medical malpractice insurance carriers. Some of these had threatened to cancel insurance on physicians who used patient arbitration agreements in their practice.

It was reported at the hearing that two malpractice carriers had withdrawn from the market and that the Argonaut Insurance Company had announced it would raise its premiums by 384 percent effective May 1, 1977. Travelers and Hartford policies which were scheduled for renewal January 1, 1976, could also expect substantial rate increases. Shortly thereafter the Argonaut Insurance Company announced it would not renew coverage on or after May 1, 1995. This affected primarily high-risk physicians in Northern California.

The Argonaut Insurance Company history is of interest. In 1954 when the CHA negotiated its group liability insurance program with Truck Insurance Exchange (TIE) it also received proposals for a new workers' compensation program. The Argonaut proposal was accepted by the CHA insurance committee and went online at the same time as the TIE liability program in 1955. At the regular quarterly meetings of the CHA insurance committee, representatives of both Argonaut and TIE were present and heard each other's presentation. The Argonaut people were so intrigued with the TIE plan that after several years they asked the committee if it would object to Argonaut developing a liability program, provided it did not compete with the CHA liability program.

This request was approved and as a result Argonaut began selling malpractice liability insurance to physicians primarily in Northern California. Then, because Argonaut was in a national expansion effort, it decided to offer such group plans in other states and was successful in Pennsylvania and New York. The New York program was a successor to the Wausau program previously set up by the New York Medical Society. In any case, the Argonaut experience was just as bad in the east as it was in California. As a part of its aggressive expansion, the company engaged in some speculative investments, which produced substantial losses and contributed to its lack of adequate capital for reserves.

Unfortunately, in the insurance commission hearings in New York and Pennsylvania these capital losses were publicized and when Argonaut was forced to withdraw from these markets in 1975 the trial lawyers jumped on this event as a basis to claim the malpractice insurance crisis of 1975 was the fault of insurance companies' investment schemes and not because of the rapid increase in frequency and severity of claims filed by plaintiff's attorneys. Such charges are repeated in literature to this date, although I know of no other carrier that had this difficulty besides Argonaut.

Another anecdote on Argonaut occurred in the 1960s. Started as a reciprocal carrier without capital stock, Argonaut initiated a corporate conversion to a stock corporation. To do this it had to distribute stock to the owners of the company, which in a reciprocal company were the insureds who received their shares of stock in proportion to each one's share of prior total paid premiums. Thus a major proportion of the stock went to participating hospitals. Ritz Heerman, when he heard about this, felt that since this was a windfall to the hospital participants they should give the stock to the insurance committee to help fund its safety programs.

As might be anticipated, the only one that agreed to do this was Ritz's own, the Lutheran Hospital Society, so the proposal promptly died. It might have been hubris, for when the stock certificates were distributed by mail, George Wood, administrator at Peralta Hospital, threw his into the waste basket, thinking it was some kind of publicity promotion.

As May 1, 1975, moved closer with the looming problem of renewals both as to cost and availability, there were rumors in the field about groups of doctors, particularly in the high-premium specialties, talking about strikes or, as they described it, withdrawals from service. The leadership of these talks came from outside the existing medical society political structure, so we had little communication with them directly or indirectly. These folk were strongly of the opinion they were not being adequately led by their existing elected officers and directors at either the state or county level.

On May 1, 1975, a major group of anesthesiologists in Northern California announced their withdrawal from service. Of course the impact on surgeries was immediate. This was followed by similar actions throughout the state in pockets such as the San Fernando Valley and Orange County in Southern California. From the hospital point of view, we were concerned about our ability to keep emergency rooms open. Then we heard the devastating news that neurosurgeons and orthopods were following the anesthesiologists. Our greatest concern was that there would be incidents of patients who died or suffered serious additional trauma from the inability to get care, with the accompanying media attention.

Initially we did not have the ability to develop a coördinated course of action or identify the demands that would bring the doctors back to practice. As we gradually set up communication the proposals took several alternative routes. One, initially popular, suggested that all physicians, as a condition of licensure, would be required to have malpractice insurance as a form of patient protection. As a *quid pro quo* for this action the Legislature would adopt a series of tort reform proposals with emphasis on the use of final and binding arbitration.

Obviously we needed something dramatic to solve this crisis. I then received a call from Fred Hiestand in Sacramento saying Governor Jerry Brown wanted to talk to me and could I come up. After a fast call to Mr. Hassard and the leaders at both the California Hospital Association and the Hospital Council of Southern California I was on my way with at least a glimmer of a plan.

Arriving at the governor's office I found a group of doctors and their spouses staked out in the governor's reception room – and at least one of them had brought a sleeping bag. Fred Hiestand met me and escorted me to a back room to meet the governor. As I recall, it was in the kitchen and we raided the refrigerator for some fruit juice for talks that went on the rest of the day. Although I had known Governor Brown on a limited basis, we got well acquainted as the three of us analyzed the situation, trying to figure out what the governor could do for the public health.

Based upon my experience with the leaders in the health field, I was convinced that assurances of legislative action would be necessary for substantial tort reform to be forthcoming. To achieve this, it would be necessary for the governor to call a special session of the Legislature to run contemporaneously with the general session. Even though I could not assure the governor this would work, because of the problems of identifying and obtaining commitments from the leadership of the dissident doctors as well as the key legislators, it seemed to me the situation had to get worse before we could take effective action. We needed to develop an accepted strategy that would save face all the way around to assure a desired result. I agreed to return to Los Angeles to see what I could work out.

Needless to say, the phones were ringing off the hook as we communicated back and forth. We not only had to agree on the design of a tort reform package that was mutually acceptable but then we had to figure out how it would be triggered. It should be noted that these problems faced by California relating to the withdrawal from practice by the high-risk physicians was developing in other parts of the country such as New York, Pennsylvania, Illinois and Florida. All of these developments brought national media attention. One advantage we had in California was the high degree of coöperation that already existed between organized medicine and hospitals. It was thus easier for us to develop a joint strategy that focused on the need for the governor to call a special legislative session to press for major reforms in both the quality of our healthcare delivery system and drastic reform of the tort system around healthcare problems, both individual and institutional.

Of overriding concern to those of us evolving the strategy was the serious possibility that any legislative measures would be immediately challenged for a violation of the equal protection clauses of both the state and federal constitutions as being limited to medical malpractice litigation and not to the total tort system relating to all personal injury actions. The obvious answer to this constitutional challenge would be to make the tort reforms applicable across the board to the entire system. However, our evaluation clearly indicated that such an approach was doomed to failure. Major business and industry would not make the necessary financial and political commitment to achieve such a result.

We had been in continual touch with the business community over the years in our attempt to get their support but their response had been lukewarm at best and we could not risk the momentum that we now had in the hopes that such help would be forthcoming. Recent activities in 1994 and 1995 at the national level on tort reform in connection with the Republican 10 Point Contract with America exemplifies the problem of attempting to integrate a total tort reform package with the inclusion of products liability and other personal injury torts with specific medical malpractice reforms.

The next issue to face as we got down to the proposal's specifics was that sacrifices, including controls on the healthcare providers, would of necessity be included in the package. Our strongly held conclusion was that specific actions must be taken on error prevention and other controls on the healthcare providers, as well as on the attorneys and plaintiffs, to enhance our chances of legislative relief. When the legislation would be tested in both the California and U.S. Supreme Courts the existence of a *"quid pro quo"* by those who benefitted could be critical in being the additional factor necessary to achieve favorable Supreme Court rulings.

Even though California does not specifically require such a *quid pro quo*, many states do, so the psychological impact is definitely there. The California Medical Association thus proposed the existing Medical Malpractice Act be completely revised to create a more effective disciplinary body with additional powers to monitor deviant practitioners, that the board itself not only be renamed but that its constituency be changed to have a majority of lay members and thus assure public accountability. The insurance industry would also be further controlled to deal with the issues of cost and availability of insurance coverage and there would be special provisions dealing with hospital care, cost and availability. And in my opinion, one of the basic factors in our ultimate success in achieving Supreme Court approval was that we treated the issue as an overall social problem of cost, quality and availability of healthcare and not as just a battle between the plaintiff's attorneys and the healthcare providers over the tort system.

Our third major strategic decision was to be careful not to overreach in our design of the package. We would include the important issues on a fair and responsible basis and be prepared to fight for the program as presented.

Then came the issue of how to trigger a settlement of the withdrawal of services by those doctors in a way that would save face for all involved. At that time the Hospital Council of Southern California had in place an official committee called the trustee advisory committee made up of hospital trustees throughout the territory. Originally organized to advise the Hospital Council board on matters dealing with organized labor and the hospital nurse strikes of the late 1960s, the committee had been quite effective but was now relatively inactive. I suggested we call this committee together and request that they, in its public responsibility for healthcare, issue a joint call to the governor, the Legislature and the doctors to take specific action – including an immediate return to service by the physicians and the calling of a special session of the Legislature on tort reform by the governor.

At the meeting with hospital trustees held on May 13, we presented this proposal and they unanimously joined in the call. Meanwhile Fred Hiestand was working with the governor, and I had made one of my quick trips to Sacramento to meet with the two of them. John Vaughn, chair of the board of trustees of Orthopaedic Hospital and a prominent local banker, took the leadership role on behalf of the trustees. The governor agreed to come to Los Angeles the following Saturday to meet with the critical players. Since the state office building was officially closed, the air conditioning was turned off and it was a particularly hot day. We divided the various groups up in separate rooms and spent some two hours negotiating the call and the return to work. I think the lack of air conditioning expedited the work, because in two hours the governor signed the special call and transmitted it to the Legislature and the press. The mutually drafted call was as follows:

PROCLAMATION

The cost of medical malpractice insurance has risen to levels which many physicians and surgeons find intolerable. The inability of doctors to obtain such insurance at reasonable rates is endangering the health of the people of this State, and threatens the closing of many hospitals. The longer term consequences of such closings could seriously limit the healthcare provided to hundreds of thousands of our citizens.

In my judgment, no lasting solution is possible without sacrifice and fundamental reform. It is critical that the Legislature enact laws which will change the relationship between the people and the medical profession, the legal profession and the insurance industry, and thereby reduce the costs which underlie these high insurance premiums.

Therefore, in convening this extraordinary session, I ask the Legislature to consider:

1. Reconstituting the Board of Medical Examiners to include a majority of public members.
2. Giving the Board full authority to discipline and decertify practitioners for lack of competency.
3. Providing the Board with authority to set recertification standards, including updated training and public service, in order to minimize malpractice and increase the quality of medical care.
4. Providing the Board with authority to develop a system to minimize the present maldistribution of medical care in certain areas of the State.
5. Establishing a Medical Peace Corps to serve Californians who lack adequate medical care.
6. Regulation of hospital rates, including authority over excessive hospital bed capacity and unnecessary duplication of expensive and under-utilized equipment.
7. Voluntary binding arbitration in order to quickly and fairly resolve malpractice claims while maintaining fair access to the courts.
8. Establishment of reasonable limits on the amount of contingency fees charged by attorneys.
9. Elimination of double payments ("collateral sources"); institution of periodic payments and reversionary trusts; limitation of compensation for pain and suffering while insuring fully adequate compensation for all medical costs and loss of earnings; and setting a reasonable statute of limitations for the filing of malpractice claims.

   In addition, I intend to:

(a) Convene a Special Panel to immediately conduct a complete investigation into all insurance company rates and reserve practices and;
(b) Support legislation in the regular session to insure adequate public representation on all professional boards, including the Board of Governors of the California State Bar.

Therefore, by virtue of Article IV, Section 3 of the Constitution, I hereby assemble the Legislature of the State of California in extraordinary session at Sacramento at 1:00 p.m. Monday, May 19, 1975, to consider and act on this legislation.

In witness whereof, I have hereunto set my hand and caused the Great Seal of the State of California to be affixed this 16th day of May, 1975.

—Edmund G. Brown, Jr., Governor of California

At this point Assemblyperson Barry Keene became a critical player in the legislative process because of his prior efforts in the 1975 general session of the Assembly to pass AB 926, which would have created an independent commission to review medical injuries using a workers' compensation type of no-fault system. His bill not only limited the plaintiff's recovery but also the plaintiff's attorney's fees, and severely restricted the patient's right to recover noneconomic losses based chiefly on "pain and suffering." The goal was to create a system of reimbursement that would effectively use the healthcare dollar and limit the escalation of costs of the existing system. But by this time his discussions with the legislative leadership and the governor had convinced him that a less drastic proposal was indicated along the lines of what became AB 1XX.

For those unfamiliar with California's legislative process, the nomenclature of AB 1XX means the bill was the first one introduced into the Assembly during the second special session of the 1975 Legislature, each X designating a special session. The desirability of a special session is that much of the formality and layers of red tape and committee structure is avoided to expedite the process. The power of special interest groups is greatly reduced—a factor which was particularly important here because of the California Trial Lawyers Association and its overriding influence with the judiciary committees in both the Assembly and the Senate.

Even with the public pressure in the media and the threat of another strike by the physicians, who kept their strike committees in full force, the Assembly judiciary committee effectively gutted some of the most important provisions. However, on the Senate side the bill was referred to the insurance and financial institutions committee which was much more favorable to healthcare providers rather than to the Senate judiciary committee. That committee essentially restored the original bill provisions in a very acrimonious atmosphere. In September the bill eventually came back to the Assembly for concurrence in the Senate version. The battle on the Assembly floor and the efforts of certain legislators to "refine" the bill lasted several days. However, the public pressure was so great that attempts by the opponents to return the bill to a conference committee failed and the bill passed by a 60 to 19 vote and was signed by the governor twelve days later in essentially the form in which it was originally drafted.

An important contribution to the favorable outcome was that representatives of the CTLA refused to negotiate with us as to the terms of the bill. Frankly, we had some "give-ups" that we would have traded for their withdrawal of opposition; however, they claimed the entire package was unconstitutional so that any participation by them in the final design of the legislation would weaken their constitutional attack. So they rolled the dice for a win or lose and fortunately for us it was a loss for them—a close loss as we shall later see. This turned out to be most significant because after the bill was passed there was a complete stand-off in the Legislature in the years that followed as to any future amendments.

What exactly did we achieve in the specific legislation and why did we draft it the way we did in collaboration with Fred Hiestand and key legislators such as Assemblyperson Keene who were taking the slings and arrows in the legislative halls? Since in many respects this was a pioneering effort in comprehensive tort reform, each provision and each word had major significance. Although it is not perfect, based on my years of drafting legislation (and more importantly living with the legislation I have drafted) I consider the result amazingly good and a tribute to both the foresight and willingness of a disparate group of us doing the drafting to make concessions for the common good. I can't emphasize this enough because the splits of opinion and the high emotional pitch of all of the constituents made being a legislator exceedingly difficult for all participants.

Needless to say, our prime objective was to draft a package of legislation that would have a serious economic and social consequence and still withstand a constitutional challenge at the California Supreme Court level. At the time, we could well anticipate that the Supreme Court would be hostile to a legislative attack on those liberal legal principles expanding the tort system that had been developed by a court that took pride in its record of creating new and innovative concepts of expanded tort liability. The court felt the burden of those changes fell upon elements of society who could most afford to pay the loss or damages. In our view, to a substantial degree, the malpractice liability crisis had been created by the courts' expansion of liability concepts at every opportunity.

Since the legislation was directed at only a narrow segment of the tort system and not the total system, the constitutional requirements of due process and equal protection clauses in both state and federal constitutions hung over the package like a big black cloud. We not only had to establish a rational basis for our proposal, but also had to show that we were acting in a fair and responsible manner. We therefore concluded the package should include sacrifices by all parties – physicians, hospitals and other healthcare providers – and also the legal profession, including both plaintiff and defense attorneys as well as the medical malpractice insurers. In order to obtain effective reform, it was important not to overreach in our zeal. Above all we should protect the plaintiff (our healthcare patient) to the fullest extent possible, so we should not be perceived as attempting to punish patients for suing physicians and hospitals.

The particular tort reform provisions achieved were these:

1. The Collateral Source Rule

The first was the new code provision, Section 3333.1, which was added to the civil code to allow the introduction of evidence on the existence of collateral sources of recovery to cover financial losses or damages to the plaintiff. The collateral source rule was a major change in tort law that had been developed over many years, going back to 1854. It had been created as a matter of social policy by the courts and not by legislative action. The rationale of the courts was that since the theory of tort law was to deter the wrongful actions of the defendants, the defendant tortfeasor should not be allowed to profit from the prudence of the plaintiff in providing for protection through the purchase of insurance.

Historically there was logic to this approach when it developed because most insurance or similar protection was solely provided by the individual and there had not developed the major social insurance programs provided through employment or governmental sources. Some academic commentators on the tort law were beginning to criticize the collateral source rule as applied to the changes in the social insurance system through the widespread availability of workers compensation, health insurance and various forms of disability insurance. Also, it was apparent they were far more cost-effective ways of covering an individual loss than the malpractice liability route. It was pointed out that substantially less than 50 percent of the malpractice insurance premium ultimately resulted in payment to the injured plaintiff, with the balance being dissipated in administrative costs, litigation costs and attorney fees.

We pointed out that to the extent that the cost of malpractice insurance was reflected in the cost of health insurance the collateral source rule duplicated the cost to all purchasers of health insurance. However, this did not settle the matter of how we should resolve the issue. The easy way was to just abolish the collateral source rule and thus permit a direct offset against the plaintiff's right to damages of the amount of the collateral sources. This is the pattern followed in most other states that have modified the collateral source rule.

Looking at the constitutional issues of due process and equal protection, we were concerned the California Supreme Court would take a dim view of this, so we came up with a different concept: rather than providing a direct offset as implemented by the trial court, we would let the availability and amount of collateral sources be introduced as evidence to the trier of fact, who could determine how it could be applied. In fairness to the injured plaintiff, to the extent the plaintiff had funded the collateral sources through personal resources, that evidence should also be available to the trier of fact. We believed the court would have a more difficult time attacking the right to know by the jury rather than the direct offset.

Interestingly enough, now that we have experience with the evidence rule of the right to know, our malpractice insurance claims people and defense counsel report that they believe they get an even better result by the disclosure to the jury of the collateral sources than they would by having the court make a direct offset. The fact that substantially all of those costs are covered by health insurance or major government programs has a major impact upon the jury by offsetting in part the emotional sympathy factor.

Taking this approach, we were then concerned with the potential that a health insurer or other collateral sources might sue the malpractice plaintiff or claim a share of the plaintiff's recovery by subrogation. This would have been an unfair result, so we included a prohibition against such subrogation in order that these costs would be borne by the health insurer or other insurer in the most cost effective manner. It is interesting to note that some states that subsequently modified their state collateral source rule overlooked the subrogation issue, but at least in the unsuccessful health reform proposal advanced by Hillary Clinton its authors picked up this important facet.

Health Policy – The Hard Way

In order to implement effectively the collateral source rule, it is necessary for the defense counsel to initiate appropriate discovery to identify all the potential sources. To assist in this process and establish a uniformity of practice, the Truck Insurance Exchange, on behalf of its insureds under the group liability program of the then California Hospital Association, commissioned Ellis Horvitz, our designated appellate counsel, to develop what has been called *The Defense Manual,* which dealt with all MICRA issues including collateral source.

With model forms for pleading the various MICRA issues, the section on collateral source was particularly important because it took four pages just to identify all of the potential collateral sources which could be explored by the defense counsel. Not only was the manual a cost saving in reference time but also was far more complete than any individual defense counsel could develop as a laundry list. The Truck Insurance Exchange made the manual available to all of its selected malpractice defense counsel and also to all defense specialists in the belief that uniformity of practice on issues such as this is in the best interest of all healthcare providers.

It remains my strong conviction that such an organized implementation of the MICRA provisions had a major impact on its favorable results and that not enough credit has been given to TIE for taking a lead on the entire MICRA issue. In fact, it is interesting to note that it took several years for all of the physician malpractice carriers to effectively utilize MICRA.

The exact language of Section 3333.1(a) and (b), the collateral source provision, is as follows:

> (a) In the event the defendant so elects, in an action for personal injury against a healthcare provider based upon professional negligence, he may introduce evidence of any amount payable as a benefit to the plaintiff as a result of the personal injury pursuant to the United States Social Security Act, any state or federal income disability or worker's compensation act, any health, sickness or income-disability insurance, accident

insurance that provides health benefits or income-disability coverage, and any contract or agreement of any group, organization, partnership, or corporation to provide, pay for, or reimburse the cost of medical, hospital, dental, or other healthcare services. Where the defendant elects to introduce such evidence, the plaintiff may introduce evidence of any amount which the plaintiff has paid or contributed to secure his right to any insurance benefits concerning which the defendant has introduced evidence.

(b) No source of collateral benefits introduced pursuant to subdivision (a) shall recover any amount against the plaintiff nor shall it be subrogated to the rights of the plaintiff against a defendant."

It is important to note that the section has not been changed since its adoption in the original MICRA legislation in 1975.

2. The $250,000 Cap on Noneconomic Damages

The most controversial provision in MICRA was the inclusion of a new Section 3333.2 in the California Civil Code placing a $250,000 cap on the recovery for noneconomic losses, as follows:

(a) In any action for injury against a healthcare provider based on professional negligence, the injured plaintiff shall be entitled to recover noneconomic losses to compensate for pain, suffering, inconvenience, physical impairment, disfigurement and other nonpecuniary damage.

(b) In no action shall the amount of damages for noneconomic losses exceed $250,000.

When this was being considered the only precedent in the U.S. was a statute adopted earlier in 1975 by the legislature and governor of Indiana. We had some problems with the Indiana statute because, although the cap was $500,000, it applied to total damages, not just the noneconomic damages. Also, part of the Indiana legislation was a patient compensation fund which provided for the payment of that portion of a judgment or settlement that exceeded $100,000.

Although we had seriously considered using a patient compensation fund with a mandatory requirement that all doctors and hospitals have a basic malpractice policy with the balance to be covered by a patient compensation fund, there was no unanimity among healthcare providers or their insurers as to the feasibility of a compensation fund in the existing California market. We were also concerned about state and federal constitutional issues relating to a cap that applied to both economic damages and noneconomic damages. In our opinion we felt we should not overreach on this.

The use of a cap limited to noneconomic damages could be justified to the public, the legislature and the courts because of an irrational pattern of judgments for noneconomic loss such as pain and suffering where there was no real standard to judge the fairness of the award, which in highly emotional cases could be astronomical. Further, trial court judges as well as the appellate courts were reluctant to exercise any realistic control over jury awards. The result was a wide diversity of award amounts depending on the whims of the individual jury.

We concluded that a simple cap on noneconomic damages that applied to the total occurrence, regardless of the number of claimants or the number of defendants, was the most effective approach with the greatest chance of success. We rejected the concept of indexing the $250,000 figure because of the bad experience with inflation that was then hitting the American economy. Thus we decided that a single legislative cap leaving complete protection to the injured plaintiff for all economic losses was the most realistic approach. We then had to wait some ten years before our judgment call was validated. This provision has been the prime target of plaintiff attorneys but has survived all substantive challenges.

3. Periodic Payment

Probably the most creative reform proposal advocated was in the addition of Section 667.7 to the code of civil procedure granting a periodic payment of medical malpractice judgments. Our interest in this concept came as a result of the suggestion of Gerald Sullivan, broker for the California Hospital Association group insurance plan. The successor to George Walker, broker for the original organization of the program, Gerry Sullivan's organization operated on a national basis, specializing in high-risk insurance packages with broad experience in providing excess insurance, primarily through the Lloyds of London market. As a result Gerry had a history in providing coverage for catastrophic losses.

A year before the MICRA legislation passed, Gerry told me of an interesting insurance market development in the South where certain railroads were experimenting with using annuities to settle catastrophic personal injury cases. They found they could produce a more constructive result for seriously injured workers and their families by assuring them an annual income for the life of the injured employee along with benefits for loss of income that continued for the use of the dependent spouse and children.

This not only protected the family from the potential waste of a large lump sum settlement (the lottery winner syndrome) through improvidence but assured that there was care for the life of the injured individual and support for the dependents of the injured party. Besides, there were beneficial tax consequences. The income to the injured party from the investment of a lump sum settlement was subject to income tax, but the payments under an annuity agreement were not.

A creative insurance person could design a plan adapted to the needs of the family, providing for special medical care, funds for college education, and the like, that the average worker could not design or provide for alone. From the viewpoint of the defendant railroad the deferral of payments under this type of program could be provided at a lower cost than could a lump sum payment.

This concept had great appeal as providing the best process designed to meet the needs of the individual plaintiff. We even hoped that since we were working with healthcare providers, they might agree to participate by providing some form of continuing care as a part of the settlement. We now know Kaiser Permanente has had favorable experience providing continued care to injured parties and we should anticipate that managed-care plans also will find it possible to do this in the future, since it is more practical for a managed-care plan to provide future care than for an individual doctor after the trauma of working out a malpractice claim.

Although it was our intent to encourage creative settlements through this process, we also recognized that unless there was some sort of legislative mandate to force the parties to consider the solution, not much would happen. In allocating the responsibility for the initial drafting of the proposal the assignment came to me to work with Gerry Sullivan on the exact language to be proposed. That language as adopted is as follows:

§ 667.7. Medical negligence actions.

(a) In any action for injury or damages against a provider of healthcare services, a superior court shall, at the request of either party, enter a judgment ordering that money damages or its equivalent for future damages of the judgment creditor be paid in whole or in part by periodic payments rather than by a lump-sum payment if the award equals or exceeds $50,000 in future damages. In entering a judgment ordering the payment of future damages by periodic payments, the court shall make a specific finding as to the dollar amount of periodic payments which will compensate the judgment creditor for such future damages. As a condition to authorizing periodic payments of future damages, the court shall require the judgment debtor who is not adequately insured to post security adequate to assure full payment of such damages awarded by the judgment. Upon termination of periodic payments of future damages, the court shall order the return of this security, or so much as remains, to the judgment debtor.

(b) (1) The judgment ordering the payment of future damages by periodic payments shall specify the recipient or recipients of the payments, the dollar amount of the payments, the interval between payments, and the number of payments or the period of time over which payments shall be made. Such payments shall only be subject to modification in the event of the death of the judgment creditor.

(2) In the event that the court finds that the judgment debtor has exhibited a continuing pattern of failing to make the payments, as specified in paragraph (1), the court shall find the judgment debtor in contempt of court and, in addition to the required periodic payments, shall order the judgment debtor to pay the judgment creditor all damages caused by the failure to make such periodic payments, including court costs and attorney's fees.

(c) However, money damages awarded for loss of future earnings shall not be reduced or payments terminated by reason of the death of the judgment creditor but shall be paid to persons to whom the judgment creditor owed a duty of support as provided by law immediately prior to his death. In such cases the court which rendered the original judgment may upon petition of any party in interest, modify the judgment to award and apportion the unpaid future damages in accordance with this subdivision.

(d) Following the occurrence or expiration of all obligations specified in the periodic payment judgment, any obligation of the judgment debtor to make further payments shall cease and any security given, pursuant to subdivision (a) shall revert to the judgment debtor.

(e) As used in this section:

(1) "Future damages" includes damages for future medical treatment, care or custody, loss of future earnings, loss of bodily function, or future pain and suffering of the judgment creditor.

(2) "Periodic payments" means the payment of money or delivery of other property to the judgment creditor at regular intervals.

(3) "Healthcare provider" means any person licensed or certified pursuant to Division 2 (commencing with Section 500) of the Business and Professions Code, or licensed pursuant to the Osteopathic Initiative Act, or the Chiropractic Initiative Act, or licensed pursuant to Chapter 2.5 (commencing with Section 1440) of Division 2 of the Health and Safety Code; and any clinic, health dispensary, or health facility, licensed pursuant to Division 2 (commencing with Section 1200) of the Health and Safety Code. "Healthcare provider" includes the legal representatives of a healthcare provider.

(4) "Professional negligence" means a negligent act or omission to act by a healthcare provider in the rendering of professional services, which act or omission is the proximate cause of

a personal injury or wrongful death, provided that such services are within the scope of services for which the provider is licensed and which are not within any restriction imposed by the licensing agency or licensed hospital.

(f) It is the intent of the Legislature in enacting this section to authorize the entry of judgments in malpractice actions against healthcare providers which provide for the payment of future damages through periodic payments rather than lump-sum payments. By authorizing periodic payment judgments, it is the further intent of the Legislature that the courts will utilize such judgments to provide compensation sufficient to meet the needs of an injured plaintiff and those persons who are dependent on the plaintiff for whatever period is necessary while eliminating the potential windfall from a lump-sum recovery which was intended to provide for the care of an injured plaintiff over an extended period who then dies shortly after the judgment is paid, leaving the balance of the judgment award to persons and purposes for which it was not intended. It is also the intent of the Legislature that all elements of the periodic payment program be specified with certainty in the judgment ordering such payments and that the judgment not be subject to modification at some future time which might alter the specifications of the original judgment.

Since there was no model to follow for such legislation I concluded that the best thing to do was avoid the regulatory approach of a detailed formula, but instead to give broad discretion to the court with a general statement of legislative intent as is set forth in the last paragraph of the act. This not only clearly explained to the Supreme Court when it reviewed the act that we were trying to be constructive in protecting the injured party but also to help guide the parties in negotiating a settlement. Our experience has been that nearly all periodic payment judgments are reached by settlement, not by court order, just as we hoped. One potential trap we had to avoid was the possibility of reopening a judgment in following years. This would have eliminated the possibility of insuring it through annuity. Therefore, the judgment is final.

Now that the law is being implemented we find there has developed a group of insurance specialists who are expert in designing and finding insurance coverage to handle these transactions. On behalf of Truck Insurance Exchange as well as several of the physician carriers, Mr. Tom Todd of the Ellis Horvitz office has become the recognized expert assisting attorneys and the courts in understanding the act and in its implementation. He has had uniform success in defending the act for us whenever it has been challenged. This approach has been copied in a number of other states and was included in the tort reform proposal that was a part of the healthcare reform package of Hillary Clinton's committee.

Following our favorable California Supreme Court decision on the constitutionality of our periodic payment statute there was greater interest nationally in this reform and as a result the commission on uniform state laws established a study on the design of a uniform state law which would utilize periodic payments. When we heard about the commission, it was well along in the drafting process. Then on seeing the draft we were concerned; it was unduly complicated, containing provisions we found unacceptable. As a result both Tom Todd and I were requested to appear before the drafting committee and make our viewpoint known. We assured them that unless the draft was substantially modified we would prefer no proposal.

After further discussions the project was ultimately dropped. When it was revived several years later we authorized Tom Todd to work with the drafting committee, which he did. The result was much better this time, except for an elaborate plan for guaranteeing the financing of the future judgment payments, which we approved. The total plan was adopted by the commission, but as far as I know no state has adopted it, although several states have adopted statutes that were modifications of the California statute.

If the concept is to be effective nationally it will probably require a federal law to preëmpt all state laws in order to avoid problems such as have recently developed in Arizona where their state supreme court in *Smith v. Meyers,* 887 P 2D 541 (1944), held the recent Arizona legislation providing for periodic payment of malpractice judgments unconstitutional as violating an Arizona constitutional requirement of payment of all judgments in a form of lump sum.

4. Statute of Limitations

A critically important section of MICRA dealt with the statute of limitations, particularly as it related to minors. This was a serious problem for hospitals, obstetricians and gynecologists because of the rapidly increasing number of what we described as "bad baby" cases. With the tremendous progress in the medical care of newborn infants, many premature newborns were being delivered alive rather than being stillborn but with a wide variety of serious medical and mental problems including major deformities. The future costs of caring for these infants was astronomical. Physicians were caught in a dilemma. If they permitted infants to die by failing to resuscitate or provide the ultimate in care through new techniques, they and the hospitals could be liable for a wrongful death. If they delivered the malformed child, they could be charged with medical malpractice. Besides, the full extent of injury to the baby might not be manifest for several years.

At this juncture the frequency and severity of infant brain damage was the fastest growing major loss area faced by both hospitals and physicians. The financial capability of the liability insurance carrier to estimate its potential liability for such cases, both known and unknown, was an impossibility under the existing law. Exposure could run until at least a year after the individual became "of age" (18 years of age now but 21 years then). There would also be the potential problem that a jury reviewing the matter more than 20 years after the occurrence would be assessing damages based on current standards rather than those in effect when the insurance carrier was collecting premiums. In making the decision to establish the age of six for the cutoff for minors, we consulted with leading neonatologists and pediatricians, who advised us that a six-year period would permit any major injury to manifest itself.

Historically the courts, particularly those in California, in practice sought to emasculate the statute of limitations so that this was also a problem in attempting to establish a fair insurance premium that would cover future losses, but not rip off the insureds. We therefore hopefully clarified the language as to the statutory date of discovery as well as spelling out the limited exceptions for fraud, intentional concealment and the presence of a foreign body which had no therapeutic or diagnostic purpose. To date this language has served its intent and survived all substantive legal challenges. The specific provision that was adopted is as follows:

§ 340.5. Three Years – Professional Negligence of Healthcare Provider. In an action for injury or death against a healthcare provider based upon such person's alleged professional negligence, the time for the commencement of action shall be three years after the date of injury or one year after the plaintiff discovers, or through the use of reasonable diligence should have discovered, the injury, whichever occurs first. In no event shall the time for commencement of legal action exceed three years unless tolled for any of the following: (1) upon proof of fraud, (2) intentional concealment, or (3) the presence of a foreign body which has no therapeutic or diagnostic purpose or effect, in the person of the injured person. Actions by a minor shall be commenced within three years from the date of the alleged wrongful act except that actions by a minor under the full age of six years shall be commenced within three years or prior to his eighth birthday whichever provides a longer period. Such time limitation shall be tolled for minors for any period during which parent or guardian and defendant's insurer or healthcare provider have committed fraud or collusion in the failure to bring an action on behalf of the injured minor for professional negligence.

For the purposes of this section:

(1) "Healthcare provider" means any person licensed or certified pursuant to Division 2 (commencing with Section 500) of the Business and Professions Code, or licensed pursuant to the Osteopathic Initiative Act or the Chiropractic Initiative Act, or licensed pursuant to Chapter 2.5 (commencing with Section

1440) of Division 2 of the Health and Safety Code; and any clinic, health dispensary, or health facility licensed pursuant to Division 2 (commencing with Section 1200) of the Health and Safety Code. "Healthcare provider" includes the legal representatives of a healthcare provider;

(2) "Professional negligence" means a negligent act or omission to act by a healthcare provider in the rendering of professional services, which act or omission is the proximate cause of a personal injury or wrongful death, provided that such services are within the scope of services for which the provider is licensed and which are not within any restriction imposed by the licensing agency or licensed hospital. Leg. H. 1970 ch. 360, 1975 Second Extra. Sess. chs. 1, 2, operative December 12, 1975.

5. Limitation on Contingency Fees

Although it is difficult to estimate the impact of a limitation on contingent fees on the ultimate cost of medical malpractice insurance premiums, there is no doubt that the issue had tremendous emotional appeal on both sides of the battle.

There were a number of factors involved in our final drafts. We first agreed there should be a descending sliding scale of the maximum charge to avoid the complaint that we were depriving patients with small claims access to the courthouse. We used 40 percent "maximum fee" as the initial figure for the first $50,000 of recovery. This actually was the figure generally demanded by most plaintiff's attorneys although some went as high as 50 percent.

Our position was that the recovery on the blockbuster judgments or settlements provided a windfall to the attorney at the expense of the injured plaintiff, who was the one who suffered the injury. Also, by adding to the share going to the injured party, the result was to substantially reduce the impact on the plaintiff's recovery created by the $250,000 limit on pain and suffering, as well as the change in the collateral source rule. As originally adopted, Section 6146 of the Business and Professions Code provided:

§ 6146. Limitations in amount –

(a) An attorney shall not contract for or collect a contingency fee for representing any person seeking damages in connection with an action for injury or damage against a healthcare provider based upon such person's alleged professional negligence in excess of the following limits:

(1) Forty percent of the first $50,000 recovered.

(2) Thirty-three and one-third percent of the next $50,000 recovered.

(3) Twenty-five percent of the next $100,000 recovered.

(4) Ten percent of any amount on which the recovery exceeds $200,000.

The limitations shall apply regardless of whether the recovery is by settlement, arbitration, or judgment, or whether the person for whom the recovery is made is a responsible adult, an infant, or a person of unsound mind.

(b) If periodic payments are awarded to the plaintiff pursuant to Section 667.7 of the Code of Civil Procedure, the court shall place a total value on these payments based upon the projected life expectancy of the plaintiff and include this amount in computing the total award from which attorney's fees are calculated under this section.

(c) For purposes of this section:

(1) "Recovered" means the net sum recovered after deducting any disbursements or costs incurred in connection with prosecution or settlement of the claim. Costs of medical care in curred by the plaintiff and the attorney's office-overhead costs or charges are not deductible disbursements or costs for such purpose.

(2) "Healthcare provider" means any person licensed or certified pursuant to Division 2 (commencing with Section 500), or licensed pursuant to the Osteopathic Initiative Act, or the Chiropractic Initiative Act, or licensed pursuant to Chapter 2.5 (commencing with Section 1440) of Division 2 of the Health and Safety Code; and any clinic, health dispensary, or health facility, licensed pursuant to Division 2 (commencing with Section 1200) of the Health and Safety Code. "Healthcare provider" includes the legal representatives of a healthcare provider.

(3) "Professional negligence" is a negligent act or omission to act by a healthcare provider in the rendering of professional services, which act or omission is the proximate cause of a personal injury or wrongful death, provided that the services are within the scope of services for which the provider is licensed

and which are not within any restriction imposed by the licensing agency or licensed hospital.

These limits were raised in 1987 in the famous "napkin compromise", discussed later. An interesting sidelight on this was that when the constitutionality of the act was before the U.S. Supreme Court the trial attorneys not only employed Harvard Law School constitution law expert Lawrence Tribe to challenge the California Supreme Court ruling upholding the constitutionality of the section but also four of the leading plaintiff's counsel in the state filed affidavits with the appellate court stating that if the constitutionality of the act was upheld they would withdraw from the practice of representing medical malpractice defendants with a result that many injured parties would be denied competent legal counsel to represent them in the future. After the U.S. Supreme Court refused to hear the appeal and the plaintiff attorneys lost their case, thus affirming the constitutionality of the provision, I asked the Truck Insurance Exchange to track their case filings to see if any of the four attorneys actually withdrew from medical malpractice practice. I was not surprised to discover they were just as active as they had been before, which appeared to validate our position that there was still a tremendous potential windfall for the attorneys.

Another issue that has bothered me on the contingent fee issue is that most trial attorneys negotiate their fee agreement directly with the injured party, taking the maximum fee without requiring the injured party to have independent counsel advising them that the provision was only a maximum and that a lower fee could be negotiated. The California Trial Lawyers Association, in its opposition to the contingent fee limit, raised the issue that there was no similar limit on the fees charged by defense counsel. To counter this argument we had included in the MICRA legislation a new Section 6146(c) to the business and professions code, providing that:

§ 6146(c). The Board of Governors of the State Bar of California shall report and make recommendations to the Legislature by July 1, 1976 on an equitable method for regulating compensation of defense counsel consistent with the policies embodied in this article, regulation of the plaintiff's attorney fees.

To no one's surprise, the State Bar ignored this direction and the section has since been dropped by the Legislature from the code. Actually, since most medical malpractice carriers in California are controlled by county medical societies or other physician groups we can assume that they have carefully monitored defense counsel fees.

6. *Notice of Intent to Sue*

One of my pet provisions put into MICRA was a new Section 364 to the California Code of Civil Procedure entitled "Notice required as condition precedent to bringing action," which says:

§ 364. Notice required as condition precedent to bringing action.

(a)   No action based upon the healthcare provider's professional negligence may be commenced unless the defendant has been given at least 90 days' prior notice of the intention to commence the action.

(b)   No particular form of notice is required, but it shall notify the defendant of the legal basis of the claim and the type of loss sustained, including with specificity the nature of the injuries suffered.

(c)   The notice may be served in the manner prescribed in chapter 5 (commencing with Section 1010) of Title 14 of Part 2.

(d)   If the notice is served within 90 days of the expiration of the applicable statute of limitations, the time for the commencement of the action shall be extended 90 days from the service of the notice.

(e)   The provisions of this section shall not be applicable with respect to any defendant whose name is unknown to the plaintiff at the time of filing the complaint and who is identified therein by a fictitious name, as provided in Section 474.

(f)   For the purposes of this section:

(1)   "Healthcare provider" means any person licensed or cer-

tified pursuant to Division 2 (commencing with Section 500) of the Business and Professions Code, or licensed pursuant to the Osteopathic Initiative Act, or the Chiropractic Initiative Act, or licensed pursuant to Chapter 2.5 (commencing with Section 1440) of Division 2 of the Health and Safety Code; and any clinic, health dispensary, or health facility, licensed pursuant to Division 2 (commencing with Section 1200) of the Health and Safety Code. "Healthcare provider" includes the legal representatives of a healthcare provider;

(2) "Professional negligence" means negligent act or omission to act by a healthcare provider in the rendering of professional services, which act or omission is the proximate cause of a personal injury or wrongful death, provided that such services are within the scope of services for which the provider is licensed and which are not within any restriction imposed by the licensing agency or licensed hospital.

I had two principal purposes in proposing this section – both going back to my early experience in reviewing claims against doctors for the Nettleship Company. What I had observed was that it was standard procedure for plaintiff's counsel to cause the initial summons and complaint to be served upon the defendant doctor by a marshal of the superior court, who would arrive at the doctor's office in uniform and badge and without prior warning would serve the papers on the doctor, generally in the waiting room. The resultant emotional impact upon the physician was often quite devastating and tended to rouse a hatred of the whole judicial tort system – and lawyers. By requiring prior written notice, a doctor was not taken by surprise and could arrange for accepting service of process by the insurance company or an attorney.

My second purpose was that by requiring a 90-day notice prior to filing the complaint there would be time, if used properly by the doctor and the insurance company, to deal constructively with the claim by either convincing the plaintiff there was no valid case or making an appropriate settlement, thus avoiding the creation of a public record of complaint against the doctor which might not have been justified. More recently, notice has triggered the possibility of an arbitration process if there was such a contractual provision.

The weakness of this requirement was that there was no effective penalty for failure to comply. After the law was passed the Truck Insurance Exchange, at my request, notified the state bar of the failure by each plaintiff counsel to give the notice. Although I had hoped for something better, the state bar at first just ignored the report, and subsequently took the official position the Legislature had no authority to impose this duty upon the bar and it would take no action. Unfortunately, this had been typical of the California State Bar Association: to ignore the medical malpractice problem because it is effectively controlled on this issue by the California Trial Lawyers Association.

For years I heard nothing more about this section, so a few years ago I asked whether we should request its repeal since it appeared to me its only benefit was in giving the plaintiff's attorney the ability to extend the statute of limitations another 90 days. When I raised this at a meeting of the counsel for the hospital and physician liability carriers, I was surprised that they unanimously opposed repeal, reporting that their claims adjusters were effectively using it in expediting early settlements just as I had hoped. It is also interesting to note that in the current discussions of medical malpractice tort reform at the national level, some of the proposed reform proposals include the notice of intent to sue.

7. *Arbitration*

Prior to the 1975 crisis the concept of using mandatory arbitration as the forum for resolving medical malpractice disputes had great support from many physician groups because of their intrinsic distrust of the fairness of the legal system and juries in particular. For them the arbitration issue was almost as important as the $250,000 cap on pain and suffering and the limit on contingent fees.

find out name of Act

California is one of the majority of states with legislation that not only authorizes the use of arbitration as an alternative method of dispute resolution, but also gives it public policy support both in legislation and court decisions. However, in spite of the expressed legislative and appellate judicial support, our experience has been that individual trial judges, and even some appellate courts, had a strong tendency to upset arbitration awards unilaterally on various technical grounds, including the doctrine of adhesion.

In order to clear the air on this issue we decided to include a provision in MICRA strengthening the support of the use of arbitration and thus, in effect, reverse some of the court decisions that had caused us trouble in the past. Since I had the most experience in developing the joint CHA/CMA arbitration project I inherited the job of drafting the new proposed Section 1295 to the California Code of Civil Procedure which, after extensive review, was ultimately passed as part of MICRA, and is set forth as follows:

§ 1295. Contract provisions.

(a) Any contract for medical services which contains a provision for arbitration of any dispute as to professional negligence of a healthcare provider shall have such provision as the first article of the contract and shall be expressed in the following language: "It is understood that any dispute as to medical malpractice, that is as to whether any medical services rendered under this contract were unnecessary or unauthorized or were improperly, negligently or incompetently rendered, will be determined by submission to arbitration as provided by California law, and not by a lawsuit or resort to court process except as California law provides for judicial review of arbitration proceedings. Both parties to this contract by entering into it are giving up their constitutional right to have any such dispute decided in a court of law before a jury and instead are accepting the use of arbitration."

(b) Immediately before the signature line provided for the individual contracting for the medical services must appear the following in at least 10-point bold red type: "Notice: By signing this contract you are agreeing to have any issue of medical malpractice decided by neutral arbitration and you are giving up your right to a jury or court trial. See article 1 of this contract."

(c) Once signed, such a contract governs all subsequent open-book account transactions for medical services for which the contract was signed until or unless rescinded by written notice within 30 days of signature. Written notice of such rescission may be given by a guardian or conservator of the patient if the patient is incapacitated or a minor.

(d) Where the contract is one for medical services to a minor, it shall not be subject to disaffirmance if signed by the minor's parent or legal guardian.

(e) Such a contract is not a contract of adhesion, nor unconscionable nor otherwise improper, where it complies with subdivisions (a), (b) and (c) of this section.

(f) Subdivisions (a), (b), and (c) shall not apply to any healthcare service plan contract offered by an organization registered pursuant to Article 2.5 (commencing with Section 12530) of Division 3 of Title 2 of the Government Code, or licensed pursuant to Chapter 2.2 (commencing with Section 1340) of Division 2 of the Health and Safety Code, which contains an arbitration agreement if the plan complies with paragraph (10) of subdivision (a) of Section 1363 of the Health and Safety Code, or otherwise has a procedure for notifying prospective subscribers of the fact that the plan has an arbitration provision, and the plan contracts conform to subdivision (h) of Section 1373 of the Health and Safety Code.

(g) For the purposes of this section:

(1) "Healthcare provider" means any person licensed or certified pursuant to Division 2 (commencing with Section 500) of the Business and Professions Code, or licensed pursuant to the Osteopathic Initiative Act, or the Chiropractic Initiative Act, or licensed pursuant to Chapter 2.5 (commencing with Section 1440) of Division 2 of the Health and Safety Code; and any clinic, health dispensary, or health facility, licensed pursuant to Division 2 (commencing with Section 1200) of the Health and Safety Code. "Healthcare provider" includes the legal representatives of a healthcare provider;

(2) "Professional negligence" means a negligent act or omission to act by a healthcare provider in the rendering of professional services, which act or omission is the proximate cause of a personal injury or wrongful death, provided that such services are within the scope of services for which the provider is licensed and which are not within any restriction imposed by the licensing agency or licensed hospital.

It should be noted that these requirements do not apply to Knox-Keene service plans (HMOs) which have their own authority to utilize arbitration. This is particularly important now that the major growth of healthcare insurance in California is through HMOs created under the Knox-Keene Healthcare Service Act. I understand that all the major HMOs in California include a broad arbitration provision as a part of their grievance procedures, and that the same pattern is developing in the rest of the country.

As a practical matter, this code section was designed to cover the types of arbitration contracts developed by the California Medical Association for use by physicians in their private practice and by the California Hospital Association for admissions signed by patients or their representative. The prime purpose was to cure the legal problems of possible adhesion which had been used by the courts to nullify an arbitration agreement between a patient, the attending physicians and the hospital. The concept of adhesion is a rule of common law, claiming that when parties enter a contract and one has substantially greater bargaining power and thus can in effect say to the other "take it or leave it," the party with the weaker bargaining power has the right to nullify the contract.

Providing the exception for HMOs (Knox-Keene Plan health service organizations) the provision recognized that the insuring contract for healthcare services was negotiated by the patient's employer who brought essentially equal bargaining power to the table so thus adhesion did not apply. This did not change the law or public policy that neither physician nor hospital could deny care to a patient who refused to sign an arbitration agreement.

Currently most hospitals have dropped their arbitration programs as have most individual physicians. However, most California HMOs as well as the physician malpractice carrier, Cooperative of American Physicians, still require arbitration as an alternative dispute resolution system and express their satisfaction with the pattern of results. The California Trial Lawyers Association continues to oppose the use of arbitration for medical malpractice claims, even though an increasing number of plaintiff attorneys are accepting the process as a method of expediting the resolution of their cases.

8. *Medical Practice Act Changes*

An important result of MICRA was the complete reorganization of the California Board of Medical Examiners and Medical Practice Act under which physicians are licensed and disciplined. Before this the board had been subject to criticism both within and without the medical profession for its perceived failures to protect the public from incompetent or fraudulent physicians. Furthermore, there was great concern within organized medicine about expanding the bureaucratic control over the practice of medicine.

The 1975 crisis created an opportunity to attack the problem constructively. It was clear to CMA that if it wanted tort reform for its physician members it would have to strengthen licensure and physician discipline. Fortunately, I had little to do with this part of the bill as Hap Hassard and Dave Willett took full responsibility for handling these legal issues and medical politics.

The entire thrust of these sections was to strengthen the licensure board's authority by giving it additional power to come up with solutions to enforce remedies against individual physicians. Public accountability was sought by adding seven public non-physician members to an expanded board of 19 members with 17 members appointed by the governor, one public member appointed by the Senate rules committee, the other by the Speaker of the Assembly.

9. *Joint Underwriting Association*

Included in MICRA were provisions creating a temporary joint underwriting association consisting of all those insurers authorized to write the state liability and medical malpractice insurance. In effect, the new organization, if established by the insurance commissioner, could in an emergency provide insurance coverage. This was to be a separate authority from the existing California Insurance Guarantee Association, which was designed to protect individuals or entities that had been insured by a company that had been declared insolvent. Fortunately, the joint underwriting association has never been implemented as the various medical societies filled the gap by creating their own captive insurance programs which continue to exist to this day.

10. The Insurance Industry

As these discussions proceeded, the California Trial Lawyers continued to blame the insurance industry for the problem. The legislative leadership in response insisted that additional reforms also be imposed upon the insurance industry, for which we fully agreed. These included sections 11587 *et seq.* of the California Insurance Code which provided:

> 1. Prohibiting insurance companies from discriminating against doctors who chose to arbitrate disputes rather than trying them in a court of law. This dealt with the action of a number of the large Eastern carriers that had refused to underwrite doctors who provided for arbitration in their patient agreements.
> 2. More important was a requirement that any insured who experienced an increase of ten percent or more in a medical malpractice premium had the right to demand a public hearing before the insurance commissioner and participate in a cross-examination of the insurance company as to the reasonableness of the proposed increase. The insurance commissioner would have access to the data necessary to make a finding as to the reasonableness of the rate and, if not, to rescind it. This for the first time made the malpractice insurance rates subject to public disclosure, a matter of great concern to the physician community. To my knowledge this provision has never been triggered, probably because nearly all malpractice insurance is written by companies created by or accountable to physicians or hospitals.

There was considerable pushing and hauling between the various Assembly and Senate committees. Probably the key to the final breakthrough and the effectiveness of the proposals was that by including the insurance proposals, the Assembly finance and insurance committee under the leadership of Barry Keene working with Fred Hiestand on behalf of the governor's office took ultimate control of the legislation from the judiciary committee, which was essentially beholden to the California Trial Lawyers. As a result we achieved stronger legislation than we ever anticipated.

This has been an abbreviated outline of the traumatic process that MICRA went through to final passage and the signature of Governor Jerry Brown. What is important is that it passed. It was a classic example of taking advantage of an open window of opportunity. If the CMA and CHA had not done the preparatory work in the 1960s and 1970s to alert the Legislature that a critical problem was developing in both the cost and availability of medical malpractice insurance, we would have faced the charge that this was only a blip in the market and no true reform was required. It was equally important that we knew what we wanted in the tort reform package, including the issues such as the restructuring of the Medical Practice Act and certain controls on the liability insurance industry. Things like MICRA do not just happen but involve a tremendous amount of work and a lot of luck.

Next we will see that our organized effort to implement MICRA effectively was a critical factor in its success. As I have observed from the tort reform endeavors in other states, it is clear they failed to do the preparatory work we did, and more importantly, they did not develop coördinated programs to produce their legislation and protect it from constitutional challenge.

18

Implementing MICRA

ICRA became effective December 17, 1975, bringing us
many challenges. A major problem was the complete
restructuring of the physician liability insurance market.
Substantially all the old mainline malpractice carriers had either
withdrawn from the California market or were in the process of
doing so. In their place were what was called "bedpan mutuals"
created and sponsored by groups of medical societies. These new
companies tended to operate in a limited territory, providing coverage for physicians who were members of the sponsoring county
medical societies. No statewide organization spoke for these physician carriers nor could they control their operation. The CMA was
the leader on physician legislative policy but had no insurance
program of its own. On the other hand, the Truck Insurance Exchange program sponsored by CHA had survived the crisis and
continued to serve the hospitals statewide and acted through CHA
on advocacy and policy issues.

Although the "bedpan mutuals" were not directly competing with each other, they were deeply involved in creating their own organizational structures and establishing a premium structure. Mostly they used the structure in effect when the commercial carriers withdrew. This was a very high premium base coupled with the requirement that each participating physician make substantial contributions to the capital of the carrier as a condition of obtaining insurance. Thus each physician had to make a large financial commitment. Since at this time interest rates were high, these companies immediately had large cash flows that went into invested reserves and surplus. For the first few years this surplus made them profitable and, more importantly, financially secure.

The CHA set up a committee through its old insurance committee structure to meet with Ken Tyler, CEO of TIE, on a regular basis to establish a strategy to protect MICRA from the impending court challenges, particularly on the constitutionality of the various provisions. We clearly recognized we would never get the full benefit of MICRA until its constitutionality was blessed by the California Supreme Court and possibly the U.S. Supreme Court.

At Ken Tyler's suggestion TIE employed Ellis Horvitz to act as its special counsel on appellate and constitutional issues related to MICRA. As Ellis had clerked at the California Supreme Court, he was a rising star in the appellate practice, primarily for insurance companies, and was asked to give his opinion on the constitutionality of MICRA. Interestingly enough, his initial reaction before doing the necessary research was that it was probably unconstitutional on the grounds of denial of equal protection and due process to victims of medical malpractice. However, when we furnished him our files of material on the buildup to the legislative action as well as the data from the experience of TIE and the department of insurance he became strongly convinced of its constitutionality and prepared a comprehensive brief on the subject with an in-depth analysis of each provision of the act. This was made available to every defense counsel handling TIE cases for the hospital association program and became the bible for all defense activity.

TIE also employed Gail Harshaw, an attorney from Oregon, to act as special coördinator for CHA/TIE's program to implement MICRA. His primary assignment was to work with the several hundred attorneys employed by TIE to implement MICRA. Since Gail was not licensed to practice in California he was no threat to California attorneys–a distinct advantage. One of his first activities was working with the Horvitz office developing *The Defense Manual*. With its comprehensive set of forms and pleadings on every issue a trial attorney could face in MICRA, this encouraged a uniform approach to critical legal issues as they developed.

Because of the danger of an outside attorney making bad law through lacking basic knowledge and research on MICRA issues, TIE authorized and paid for the distribution of the manual to all defense attorneys handling MICRA cases, regardless of whether they handled TIE cases or not. This was tremendously important because there was no similar program yet developed among physician carriers. Gail then traveled throughout California visiting TIE defense counsel offices instructing them how to use the manual as well asking them to share with Gail and Ellis their own research and pleading materials for inclusion in future update issues of the manual. These various attorneys were then given credit for their contributions as the defense manual was periodically updated.

Next Gail set up semiannual weekend conferences with TIE defense counsel to review experiences in implementing MICRA. My part was to attend each conference and give a 20-minute presentation on behalf of the hospital association. Although I discussed tort reform from a legislative strategy viewpoint, my role was to make them feel part of the cause of healthcare by understanding the problems, at both national and state levels, of such programs as Medicare and Medicaid. The psychology of the presentation was to get them concerned and knowledgeable about the future of the hospitals they were representing and be a part of the healthcare team. This worked well and I got calls from individual attorneys throughout the state wanting to talk out local issues with me, showing concern for their individual hospital clients far beyond their role in defending malpractice actions. This also was the result of assigning claims managers plus outside legal counsel to each participating hospital, thus assuring expert advice and helping develop a strong identification by the attorney with the assigned hospitals. Although our top priority was to get a decision by the California Supreme Court establishing the constitutionality of MICRA, we continued to handle a wide variety of decisions by trial courts and intermediate appellate courts. By various maneuvers we actually got cases to the California Supreme Court on three instances, but in each case the court refused to accept the matter or to rule on the constitutionality issues of MICRA. Thus we did not enjoy the full impact of MICRA and continued to worry about what would happen if any substantial part of MICRA were declared unconstitutional. This had major financial implications for both TIE and the physician carriers as they had to maintain large reserves to cover potential losses on cases in process as well as those that had not yet been reported. Since TIE continued to write its policies on an occurrence basis, it meant it had a large exposure of long-tail cases that had developed both before and after MICRA was enacted.

I might interject that the difference between an "occurrence" policy and a "claims made" policy is that under the first kind, the insurance policy covers all claims that may be made for any tort during a policy year by the insured regardless of how many years after the occurrence it may have been reported to the insurance carrier. This leads to the long tail on reporting claims, particularly on such occurrences as infant brain damage cases. A claims made policy covers those tort claims reported during the policy year without responsibility for claims arising during that year but not reported for any of a variety of reasons. This process substantially reduced the long tail on reported claims; however, it does defer the cost of late reported claims to future years. It was decided by the CHA insurance committee, and agreed to by TIE, to maintain an occurrence policy form as long as possible so they could shift to a claims made form in the event of a future crisis. Actually, the claims made option was later offered to hospitals. I have always preferred the occurrence form for insuring hospitals, although I do accept the need for the claims made form for physicians.

❦ American Bank & Trust Case

In 1980 a district appeals court in San Francisco finally ruled on the constitutionality of the periodic payment section of MICRA and by a unanimous decision held the section was unconstitutional on grounds it violated the federal constitution (Articles 5 and 14 relating to equal protection and due process). The appellate court upheld a trial court decision invalidating the section by concluding:

> We agree that to find that the protection and special dispensation given to health delivery tortfeasor is in the best interest of public health is illogical to the point of irrationality.

So it was on to the California Supreme Court, which granted a hearing on May 29, 1980. The critical time had arrived and we had to make the Supreme Court, then led by Rose Bird as chief justice, see the merits of our position. If the choice had been ours, the periodic payment section would not have been the one to reach the Supreme Court. Not only did it have the equal protection matter as the key issue to be decided but there was also the question of the role of the trial court in applying the periodic payment requirement as denying the right to trial by jury by substituting an annuity in the place of the traditional lump sum award. This has been fatal in similar cases in other states in recent years.

As we attempted to predict a vote count on the court of seven justices we knew Chief Justice Rose Bird was strongly opposed to tort reform as was Justice Stanley Mosk. We had varying degrees of hope as to the others, but Justice Richardson, who we felt was favorable to our position, recused himself from the panel because his son, a lawyer, had done some legal work for the Farmers Insurance Group, the parent corporation of the Truck Insurance Exchange. Later in the process Justice Cruz Reynosa, a new Brown appointee, also recused himself because as a member of the district court of appeal he had ruled favorably on the constitutionality of the MICRA statute section limiting the contingent fees for plaintiff's attorneys. We were faced with the fact that it was the prerogative of Chief Justice Bird, as chairperson of the judicial counsel, to designate the replacements for each recused justice.

On the status of Chief Justice Rose Bird we had a real problem. In 1975 when MICRA was passed and transmitted by the Legislature to Governor Brown for his approval or veto, Ms. Bird was at that time in Governor Brown's cabinet as Secretary for Human Welfare. It was rumored she had actively opposed MICRA and we confirmed this by a request under the Freedom of Information Act which disclosed she had written a strong memo to Governor Brown urging him to veto the MICRA legislation.

The question was how to use that information. As a matter of law she did not have to recuse herself even if we formally challenged her participation in the case. Even if she decided to recuse herself, as chief justice she would be the one to select her replacement. After numerous telephone calls back and forth and much soul searching we concluded it would be a greater risk to raise the problem than to keep quiet. Later someone leaked it in the press but we still took no action and she ignored the matter and actively participated in the decision of the court to our detriment.

How to handle the briefing was the question. Obviously, both the trial court's and the court of appeal's opinions showed neither was convinced that a true crisis existed in 1975 when MICRA passed – nothing that justified limiting the rights of injured plaintiffs in medical malpractice cases but not in other types of personal injury actions. Unless we could convince the Supreme Court panel that the crisis in 1975 was real, we were doomed to failure.

Therefore our strategy was for the CMA and CHA to be responsible for the master briefs treating the legal and factual issues in-depth, with Ellis Horvitz taking the lead on this effort. We proceeded to recruit amicus briefs from various sectors of the health field as to their special problems created by the malpractice tort system and what MICRA had done to ameliorate these in the public interest. We wanted each brief to make a strong presentation from the experience of its constituents and not to attempt to rehash the legal issues that would be covered in the master brief.

We were successful in obtaining briefs from the University of California on behalf of its teaching hospitals statewide, the Los Angeles County Board of Supervisors on behalf of its hospitals and medical programs as well as the county hospitals throughout the state, the Association of District Hospitals, a group of religious-sponsored nonprofit hospitals and, of course, both the CMA and CHA. These were well-drafted briefs with a minimum of duplication. On the other hand, the CTLA filed a number of repetitive briefs claiming there was no problem that needed to be resolved.

The oral argument followed and it was impossible for us to count votes among the justices so all we could do was wait. Not until March 31, 1983, did we get notice of the decision – four-to-three against us with the opinion written by Justice Mosk. Chief Justice Bird and Justices Rattigan and Racanelli joined in the majority opinion. The latter two were appointed by the judicial council headed by Rose Bird as substitutes for Justices Reynosa and Richardson. However, a strong dissenting opinion was filed by Justice Kaus, joined by Justices Broussard and Feinberg, the latter also an appointee by Justice Bird as chair of the judicial council.

As pointed out by the dissent, the majority had substantially based its opinion on the fact that the enactment of MICRA was conceived to reduce or contain overall costs of medical care and hospital care. In fact, although medical malpractice premiums had been reduced by 25 percent during the years following the passage of MICRA, overall healthcare costs had continued to increase. Thus, there was no constitutional justification for legislation which deprived injured parties of certain rights.

We, of course, were devastated by the decision, particularly the peculiar approach to constitutional law taken by the majority. Fortunately for us, the decision received immediate attention in the legal media and the reported analysis was generally critical of the Mosk opinion. Our problem was whether to ask the court for a rehearing and, if so, what the prospects might be. A quick study of the court's prior actions indicated that until then the Rose Bird Court had never reversed one of its own decisions based on the substance of the decision. However, we had no choice but to try.

It was of great importance that in the intervening time Governor Brown had appointed Joseph R. Grodin to the court to take the place of Justice Racanelli, one of the majority in the Justice Mosk decision. Our chance for a reversal depended on how Justice Grodin might vote. Since we really had no choice, we requested a rehearing, which was granted on June 15, 1983. Again we waited interminably until July 9, 1984 – when the court handed down a 28-page opinion written by Justice Otto Kaus upholding by a four-to-three vote the constitutionality of MICRA and the section on periodic payments in particular. Justices Broussard, Grodin and Feinberg joined in the opinion while Justice Mosk and Chief Justice Bird each wrote bitter separate dissenting opinions.

The Justice Kaus opinion furnished the basis for subsequent decisions on various provisions in MICRA, all of which were eventually sustained. For the first time we had the full benefit of the MICRA statute – a long ten years after the original enactment of the statute. Consequently, the medical malpractice insurance market has stabilized in the state, but California is no longer known as the

Health Policy – The Hard Way

state with one of the worst litigation records and highest premiums. Prior to the adoption of MICRA, California was always listed in this category along with New York and Michigan. In a 1995 study of physician premiums published by the Physician Insurance Association, compared to California only 16 states had lower insurance premiums for internists, 17 states for general surgeons, and 20 for OB/GYN specialists – an amazing shift when you realize what a litigious state California continues to be.

❧ *Amicus Committee*

I cannot emphasize enough that it was not just the passage of MICRA that produced the favorable results. The follow-up organized support was of enormous import. Gail Harshaw, on behalf of TIE, with all defense counsel worked on a mutual support basis in critical litigation. Following the Supreme Court decision in the *English* case this effort by Gail was given official status by the CMA and CHA through the creation of the amicus committee. The major malpractice insurance carriers were invited to join the committee and make an annual contribution to its legal defense fund, which would be used to employ counsel to prepare and file amicus briefs in all critical cases involving MICRA and related issues.

There was need for this support because during the period prior to the *English* decision the California Trial Lawyers Association directed its fire on the constitutional issue, but after losing the *English* case their attention was directed toward finding in the actual tort reform provisions loopholes or weaknesses that could emasculate the legislation. Their special ire was directed at the $250,000 cap on pain and suffering and the limit on contingent fees. First they claimed there should be multiple $250,000 limits for multiple plaintiffs, or multiple defendants, or multiple causes of action, and many other similar issues. The CMA under Catherine Hanson and more recently under Gregory Abrams assumed the administration of the committee, which meets by conference call

Patient Protection Act

every two months to review pending litigation and authorize, where indicated, an amicus brief. This process has been very active and quite successful on the litigation side with no major cases lost.

❦ *Californians Allied for Patient Protection*

Equal concern has been given as to potential legislative activity in the field of tort reform, either affirmatively or defensively. First, it is recognized that MICRA did not do a complete job and if the opportunity becomes available, the healthcare providers should be prepared to act. More importantly, there continue to be attempts to repeal all or part of MICRA at either the legislative level or by an initiative sponsored by the CTLA.

To meet these threats an independent organization known as Californians Allied For Patient Protection (CAPP) has been created with a dues-paying membership of over a hundred organizations to deal with these political issues. The total membership meets several times a year and it has a very active committee structure. The special committees continue to study tort reform issues and have prepared model legislation and initiatives to be available if needed. The staff and the members actively relate to individual legislators to keep them posted on important tort reform issues.

One matter it handled became known as the "napkin truce." Some of the leading legislators, particularly Willie Brown, then Speaker of the Assembly, were concerned about the possibility of an open fight between the CTLA and the CMA/CHA over tort reform with the potential threat of possible state initiatives. Legislators were concerned this feud would waste precious political funds on initiatives instead of supporting their own election coffers.

It was decided to invite several legislators and representatives of CAPP to an informal dinner to discuss a possible truce where the parties negotiated a deal by horse-trading on legislative action on issues of importance to each. The CAPP side was given a much stronger limitation on punitive damages in exchange for an agreement that they would not support an initiative for the following three years. For the same chip the CTLA bargained for and got support for an increase in their percentage contingent fees at the expense of their patient clients. The agreement was written on a napkin, thus the name of the truce. The agreed-to legislation was passed and the truce respected, but it has now run out. When the deal became known to the media, interestingly enough the consumer press was critical of the CTLA for negotiating an increase in their contingent fees while getting nothing for their injured clients.

During and after the truce period the battle ground shifted to the national level when Hillary Clinton in 1994 created a massive task force to develop a national healthcare reform package. As this project developed, it appeared that as part of the cost savings provision there could be included national medical malpractice tort reform that would preëmpt state laws.

In 1994 members of the executive committee of CAPP urged the organization to become actively involved in the federal legislation proposals and offer the benefit of the California experience with MICRA to help design the federal proposals. We wanted to be sure no action taken at the federal level would adversely affect MICRA. As a result a drafting committee of four was selected – Phil Hinderberger, Dave Willett, Charles O'Brien and myself. Phil and Dave were also appointed to the national coalition drafting committee. As a committee we not only proposed specific language to be included in any federal healthcare reform legislation but also a set of provisions that could be used in drafting state legislation in the event the federal legislation failed – which it did. These model provisions were designed to cure the weaknesses that we had identified in MICRA during the past 20 years.

The biggest issue in this drafting process was defining "healthcare provider". Under our MICRA legislation we designed the act to protect the licensed direct providers of healthcare such as physicians, hospitals, nurses, etc., but it did not cover such elements of the healthcare feeding chain as pharmaceutical or medical device manufacturers, nor did it protect health insurers or most managed-care plans except HMOs. In our 1994 drafting effort we ran into opposition from the fee-for-service medical community that opposed any expanded liability reform protection to insurers or managed-care plans. This issue put the AMA in the middle. Then the pharmaceutical manufacturers had their own ideas about how to define a punitive damage provision. Probably there will again be some activity at the national level, but with the result of 1996 elections it is doubtful if anything of substance will pass until there is another crisis in healthcare.

For the long run it would be a distinct advantage to California healthcare providers to have federal preëmptive legislative provisions because it would be much harder for CTLA to emasculate federal legislative action where there is no initiative process. MICRA is and always will be an example of Health Policy – The Hard Way. Hopefully, I can continue to remain active in the current battles over the need for an effective grievance procedure not only for patients but others in the administration of managed-care plans. In my opinion the use of a competent grievance procedure giving the patient or other complainant a fair and productive forum leading to final and binding arbitration will have a substantial impact on the liability issues of the total healthcare process.

The future legislative and legal issues relating to quality of care as well as medical malpractice will be litigated over matters relating to managed care and its potential abuses of denying needed care to insured patients. Unfortunately, Congress in adopting the Employee Retirement Income Security Act, made its provisions applicable to employee health benefit plans. This has created great confusion in the courts as to the applicability of its provisions to malpractice tort litigation against all parties in the feeding chain of healthcare. Because of the sensitivity of ERISA Congress has been unwilling to reopen the issue and clarify the liability issues.

19

Arbitration

I am strongly committed to the merits of using arbitration for medical malpractice disputes even though my attempts to get the process fully implemented in California hospitals have been less than a success. However substantially all the major managed-care plans and HMOs now include an arbitration provision in their subscription agreement, following the pattern established by the Ross-Loos Medical Plan and Kaiser Permanente years ago. With the recent California legislation requiring three strikes and you are out (life term) in criminal cases, the courts are now increasingly overloaded with criminal trials, so the extended delays in reaching trial in civil cases is further protracted and arbitration is looking better as an answer to getting these cases resolved to assure the continued insurability of both hospitals and physicians.

At a critical meeting of the California Hospital Association insurance committee in 1968, we discussed the problems created by the continued increase in the number of "bad baby" cases and the fact that the delay in settling these catastrophic cases could adversely affect the availability of liability insurance for hospitals. (This was, of course, before the adoption of MICRA in 1975 which reduced the statute of limitations on claims for infant birth injuries from 18 years to eight years.) At that time the problem faced by the CHA insurance committee and the Truck Insurance Exchange in their jointly sponsored program was how to establish a realistic premium structure while at the same time prudently reserve for losses from yet unreported infant birth injury cases that might be filed up to 18 or more years later, plus an additional four or five years before getting to trial. These were potentially catastrophic cases for both the TIE and the excess carriers at Lloyds of London.

In any event, as I reviewed the day's results on the plane back from San Francisco it occurred to me that perhaps we could use arbitration as a way of expediting the resolution of these cases. The next morning I asked my associate, Ted McCabe, to draw up a simple arbitration clause that we might introduce into the conditions of admission forms signed by the patient at the hospital. Two weeks later I received a ten-page memorandum outlining his research on the issue, pointing out the legal and administrative problems we would face.

When I shared the memorandum with Mr. Hassard in his capacity as legal counsel to the CMA, he responded that the doctors would be interested in coöperating in a demonstration project on the use of arbitration. This led to extended discussions on the design of the undertaking and specifically how to face the issues brought up in the McCabe memorandum.

Initially our biggest dilemma was dealing with the legal doctrine of adhesion, which might be held as a basis for invalidating the arbitration clause. We were particularly concerned with the 1963 California Supreme Court decision of *Tunkl v. Regents of University of California,* 32 CAL. RPTR. 33, a 1963 California Supreme Court case in which the court held that a provision in the conditions of admission agreement at the University Hospital, specifying that the patient waived any right to claim negligence against the University Hospital was invalid, because it violated the rule of adhesion and was an unconstitutional requirement. As succinctly stated by the Supreme Court, "The admission room of a hospital contains no bargaining table...." and the court rules that it was unfair for the university to require such a waiver as a condition of admission to the hospital. Our problem was whether or not the court would apply the same rule to a hospital-initiated mandatory arbitration agreement.

Although the courts regard the use of arbitration with favor, we anticipated that this unilateral action by a hospital or physician denying the patient a right to a trial by jury would be constitutionally challenged as depriving the patient of due process. Our proposed solution to this obstacle was commonly referred to as the "opt-out" provision which was included in the arbitration clause by a stipulation that the patient could, in effect, knock out the arbitration clause simply by putting a check mark in the box printed on the admission agreement. We also granted the patient 30 days after signing the conditions of admission form in which to nullify the agreement to arbitrate by simple written notice to the hospital. This approach relied on the legal doctrine that even if a person signs an agreement without fully understanding its terms, if that party is given a copy of what has been signed and has a reasonable time to invalidate it, that person becomes bound by it regardless of whether they understood the provision at the time of signing it.

Our next predicament was how to administer the program and what form of arbitration should be used. Under California arbitration law, each party designated an arbitrator and if the two arbitrators did not agree as to the resolution of the issues then they jointly would select a third arbitrator whose decision was final. The physician representatives reported a concern by the physicians that such a process would lead to compromise in negotiated settlements. The physicians wanted a clear-cut decision as to whether or not they had been liable for negligence, because they believed that a decision by a qualified panel of arbitrators would be more fair to physician defendants as contrasted with decisions made by jury panels, which they felt could be emotional and erratic.

We then met with the representatives of the American Arbitration Association to find out their views and see whether the AAA would be interested in administering the program as an independent body. They were most interested and assured us that their system was designed to reach a final decision on the merits of each case and not as a negotiated compromise.

Under the AAA process, except for small cases, three arbitrators are selected by the parties from three separate panels provided by the AAA – one panel of attorneys, another from business or other disinterested parties and the third of medical experts in the field being arbitrated. The administrator of the program submits lists from each panel to the parties, who indicate their order of preference from each panel. When the results are received the administrator lines up the results to get the closest mutual preference of both parties.

The AAA also suggested that if we selected AAA to administer the program they would work with us in developing a special set of rules dealing with the peculiarities of a malpractice arbitration, including the fact that there would probably be multiple defendants such as the hospital and doctors as well as possible suppliers of medical devices or supplies. Also spelled out was the fee schedule and a provision that if the amount involved was less than $20,000 a single arbitrator would be selected. The problem of involving additional parties who did not sign the original agreement was resolved by establishing a procedure under which they could participate.

After discussing the project with the Truck Insurance Exchange, the carrier for the hospital liability insurance program, and the major physician insurance carriers, we had their blessing to proceed, with their assurance they would not deny insurance coverage to any insured hospital or physician who participated. Although several of them were not enthusiastic about this development, they went along with the agreement and at least one, the Cooperative of American Physicians, strongly urged their insureds to use arbitration. The CMA and CHA then jointly endorsed the use of the American Arbitration Association administration of the demonstration project.

We proceeded to prepare the language to be placed in the conditions of admission form to be signed by the patient or the patient's representative, as follows:

> Arbitration Option: Any legal claim or civil action in connection with this hospitalization, by or against the hospital or its employees or any doctor of medicine agreeing in writing to be bound by this provision, shall be settled by arbitration at the option of any party bound by this document in accordance with the Commercial Arbitration Rules of the American Arbitration Association and with the Hospital Arbitration Regulations of the California Hospital Association (copies available at hospital admission office), unless the admitting physician has not agreed in writing to be bound by this provision, or unless patient or undersigned initials below or sends written notification to the contrary to the hospital within thirty (30) days of the date of patient discharge.
>
> If patient, or undersigned, does not agree to the "Arbitration Option," then he will initial here.

This language was broad enough to include all possible disputes between the hospital and the patient, including fee or charge disputes. At the same time the CMA developed model forms to be used by physicians in connection with their office practice.

Having covered all of these issues we then set out to establish the demonstration project in Southern California and the following hospitals agreed to participate:

California Hospital, Los Angeles
Daniel Freeman Memorial Hospital, Inglewood
Garfield Hospital, Monterey Park
Holy Cross Hospital, San Fernando
Hospital of the Good Samaritan, Los Angeles
Long Beach Community Hospital, Long Beach
Memorial Hospital of Glendale, Glendale
South Bay Hospital, Redondo Beach

It was my job to go out and meet with the hospitals to explain the program and respond to questions, particularly from the medical staff and governing board, as to what to expect. We had also prepared a model questionnaire card to be given to members of the medical staff to indicate whether or not they would participate in the program along with the hospital. This led to a lot of night meetings at the various hospitals in which I presented the goals of the arbitration project as follows:

- To speed the handling of claims so that they can be disposed of in months rather than years.
- To reduce substantially the time a physician must spend in litigation.
- To save the time of physicians, witnesses, and lawyers.
- To ensure a high degree of sophistication in the decision-making process.
- To minimize unnecessary appeals because of the recognized finality of an arbitration award.
- To limit publicity because of the confidential nature of the arbitration process as contrasted with the flamboyant aspects of many jury trials.
- To limit the amount of judgments, which otherwise might be too large because of emotional and theatrical appeals to a jury.

The project began in July of 1969, and when we had a progress meeting a year later we learned that only 50 persons out of the 70,000 hospital admissions had rejected the arbitration option, including three who did so by written notices during the 30-day period of opt-out. No suits had been filed in which a request for arbitration had been filed, which was not surprising in view of the delays inherent in such litigation. We then opened up the project to general participation and many more hospitals from all parts of the state joined, so that ultimately more than a hundred hospitals were participating.

Another year passed and I got in touch with Gail Harshaw at TIE to find out what was happening in the litigation part of the program. He reported that little, if any, action had occurred at the trial court level. More importantly, it was clear that our own defense counsel appointed by TIE were finding every excuse possible to avoid initiating arbitration in lieu of court trials. Only a small group of attorneys were supportive. It was quite apparent that our own defense attorneys were reluctant to learn a new process for resolving malpractice disputes and were sabotaging the program.

At our request the TIE claims department began to press the attorneys to initiate demands for arbitration. Thus more cases went to arbitration but still the results were spotty. However, both hospitals and individual physicians gradually lost interest and very few continue to use the arbitration language in their conditions of admission forms. Of incidental information is that our informal survey on who opted out of arbitration at the time of admission was that the largest group consisted of lawyers' secretaries and lawyers' spouses, although lawyers themselves routinely stayed in. More recently I have received reports that now it is school teachers who are most likely to opt out.

It has been my experience in working with physicians that they place great reliance on material they read in the medical journals. This is a natural result of their training in the importance of keeping up-to-date on the latest development in their field of practice. As a matter of legal jurisprudence this is an important test of their fulfilling their standard-of-care requirement. Therefore, when I want to get the attention of the physician community I try to arrange for an appropriate article to be published. In this case Mr.

Hassard and I jointly wrote an article entitled "Arbitration" for *Hospitals,* the journal of the American Hospital Association, (Vol. 44, Oct. 3, 1970) in which we described the California demonstration project and included the questions we were seeking to answer by the project, which were:

> Will the availability of arbitration increase the number of claims?
> Will settlements be encouraged or discouraged?
> Will a sophisticated arbitration panel award larger judgments than a jury might?
> Will an arbitration panel tend to render compromise verdicts in cases where liability is doubtful?
> How will cost of defense of an arbitration case compare with the cost of a court litigated case?
> What happens when one physician agrees to arbitrate and another does not?
> Does the arbitration clause apply to fee disputes?
> How is the process of discovery to be handled?
> How are judgments to be allocated among defendants?
> If a patient dies, is the executor bound by the agreement for arbitration?

In the June 1976 edition of *Inquiry,* Duane H. Heintz, MHA, director of finance and insurance for the Iowa Hospital Association, published an in-depth study of the California project in which he concluded:

> In summary, the findings of this study indicate that the simple existence of an arbitration option and the logistical systems supporting it have produced positive results and have established significant trends in a group of hospitals participating in the Southern California arbitration project when compared to a group of Southern California hospitals that have not participated.

The CMA developed a separate project for using arbitration in physicians' offices which included a pamphlet explaining the use of arbitration to patients with model consent forms to be signed by the patients. Where actually pressed by the insurance carriers, such as the Cooperative of American Physicians, this appears to have been a success.

I continue in my belief that this process is a good substitute for courthouse litigation. In part my support is based on personal experience acting as an American Arbitration Association volunteer arbitrator in a couple of major construction disputes. I was particularly impressed with the efficiency of the process in reducing legal costs to the parties, and of even greater importance, I was very conscious of the intent of the three arbitrators to find and achieve justice. It was not a beauty contest by competing attorneys to see who could win a victory over the other.

With but a few exceptions, plaintiff lawyers have continued to fight the use of arbitration, evidently in the belief they will get better results from the jury system. Consequently they have attacked the Kaiser Permanente program, particularly as to its administration. For example, in one case they overturned an arbitration because the neutral arbitrator in that particular case had acted in the same role in a number of Kaiser cases. The plaintiff claimed this was prejudicial as the arbitrator would be induced to favor Kaiser Permanente to receive future appointments.

In another recent case it was charged that the administrator of the Kaiser program had intentionally delayed the arbitration process so that the named plaintiff would die before the matter could be arbitrated, to the detriment of the plaintiff's family. These cases emphasize the importance of fair administration, particularly when performed in-house instead of by an independent administrative agency such as the American Arbitration Association. However, in fairness I should point out that there were also questions by the hospital participants in the original CHA/CMA program as to the quality of the arbitrators provided by the AAA, probably as a result of our failure to monitor the program effectively.

It is my expectation that with the movement to managed healthcare and the need for constructive grievance procedures that arbitration will be more successfully utilized by all participants in the healthcare feeding chain to settle disputes, both between the parties as well as with patients.

Although not of particular importance to California, a state that has a public policy of encouraging arbitration, I should point out that the U.S. Supreme Court in a January 18, 1995, decision, *Allied-Bruce Terminix Co. v. Dobson*, (115 S. CT. 1995), held that the Federal Arbitration Act, which makes enforceable a written arbitration provision in "a contract evidencing a transaction involving commerce," preëmpts and makes invalid an Alabama Supreme Court decision upholding an Alabama anti-arbitration statute. This decision will be important in states that have anti-arbitration statutes and desire to use arbitration programs such as we have initiated in California.

20

Guiding Principles for Hospitals

Before going on, I would like to point out the historical role of the Hospital Council of Southern California (HCSC), whose name changed in January 1995 to the Healthcare Association of Southern California (HAEC), its evolving constituency and its role on behalf of healthcare providers. During my 55 years' experience with HCSC as both its general legal counsel and member of its board, executive committee and many of its ad hoc and standing committees, I have enjoyed a privileged position from which to observe both its staff and volunteer leadership.

With all of the many volunteer organizations in various capacities with which I have worked over the years, I can say without reservation that HAEC has been unique in the role it filled on behalf of hospitals, but more importantly of patients. The council has been dedicated to quality care at a fair and reasonable cost. Furthermore, it has acted as the conscience of hospitals in Southern California in its relationship to the community. As an organi-

zation it has been blessed with strong leadership by its staff. That
has given it an uncommon ability to stay ahead of the power
curve. By this I mean it has not only understood the external forces that would adversely affect the ability of hospitals and physicians to perform their roles but has acted to meet these trends.
Further, although most of the programs I will describe originated
in Southern California, they soon spread statewide under the leadership of the California Hospital Association.

In 1958 under the leadership of Glenn Ebersole, the Hospital
Council developed "The Guiding Principles for Hospitals" in response to widespread media criticism of hospital charging practices
and rapidly increasing hospital care costs. Of great annoyance to
the public had been the complexity of hospital bills as well as the
widespread use of nuisance charges, such as a record fee ($3 to $5),
tongue blades (25¢), patient gowns ($2), common sitz bath ($5),
proctoscope rental ($3), and the 50¢ aspirin tablet. Instead of an
all-inclusive room charge, up to 60 to 70 percent of a patient's bill
was made up of ancillary charges. Even health insurance companies
made no sense of hospital bills nor could they effectively compare
the charges of one hospital against another. This was 1958, long
before the present nationwide criticism of hospitals developed.

Under the Hospital Council's Guiding Principles each participating hospital was required to:

> 1. Provide a uniform system for establishing rates – so that
> items like employee services, equipment and supplies would be
> included in the basic charge for each service.
> 2. Provide hospital bills which could be easily understood by
> patients and group purchasers.
> 3. Establish hospital charges that would be equitably related to
> the cost of providing each service.
> 4. Demonstrate good faith by each hospital making a schedule
> of its charges available for examination by patients and other
> interested parties.
> 5. Establish a grievance procedure whereby grievances against a
> hospital could be properly adjudicated and processed.

Health Policy – The Hard Way

The statement went on to spell out in detail which items could be charged separately as well as those to be included in the basic room charges and basic surgery charge. Also delineated were the ethical responsibilities of the governing board and the medical staff in maintaining quality of care and responsible management by including a commitment to nondiscriminating admitting procedures and a requirement that all emergency patients receive first-aid treatment regardless of financial status. Although many of these requirements were considered quite radical at the time, the council board accepted the document and made it policy for its members.

Following the adoption of this statement the Hospital Council paid for ads in the area's major newspapers announcing the Guiding Principles and the existence of a grievance procedure established by the council to which individual patients as well as health insurers could present their complaints. With the grievance committee created, the complaints flowed in. Experience indicated that four out of five complaints could be adjusted by the council staff directly with the hospital administration, but in the first year some 200 were referred to the grievance committee, which found 53 percent justified, with appropriate adjustments in bills or procedures implemented.

The importance of this process became evident when three years later a bill was introduced in the Legislature requiring the filing of scheduled hospital fees and charges with the state department of public health – just the kind of bureaucratic legislation we had feared. Sam Tibbitts, president then of the council, and I appeared before the Assembly subcommittee on hospitals and medical facilities on November 3, 1961, to oppose the legislation and used as the basis for our testimony a report on the Guiding Principles plan. As a result the committee found that the conditions which might have warranted legislation had been largely alleviated and they killed the bill. About this time the president of the American Hospital Association called the Guiding Principles "the most important document of the decade."

The Guiding Principles for Hospitals plan, and in particular its grievance procedure program, continued successfully for about ten years until HCSC received a strong letter from the office of Evelle Younger, then California attorney general, demanding that the council cease and desist in its enforcement of the Guiding Principles through its grievance procedures as being a conspiracy to interfere with the business practice of its individual members, a violation of state law, and included various other complaints of practices he considered in the nature of price fixing.

We had known we were getting close to the legal limit as our committee had become tougher and tougher. As a result, we acceded to the demand of the attorney general and dissolved the grievance procedure. However, the process had accomplished its purpose in greatly improving the relationship between hospitals and the public as well as with health insurance companies and became the basis for other HCSC programs.

Other Guiding Principle-type documents that the Hospital Council subsequently adopted included "Principles for Planning Hospital Service," December 22, 1960; "Code of Ethics on Recruitment Practices for Hospitals," August 27, 1962; and "The Guideposts for Hospital Personnel Practices," also from August of 1962. All these were designed to solve healthcare provider and policy issues without government intervention and were truly the creation of hospital policy by voluntary action.

Guiding Principles for Physician/Hospital Relationships

The benefits of a positive voluntary action program soon became obvious. In August of 1957 Jane and I took our two sons on a two-week trip to the East to visit Jane's hometown, Boston, and her family and to show the boys Eastern colleges to apprise them of those educational opportunities when it came time for them to go to college. (Eventually they both went to California colleges.)

We were in New York sightseeing and had just returned to our hotel after touring the United Nations Center on Thursday afternoon just before Labor Day weekend. I found a stack of pink telephone messages at the desk requesting I call a variety of people from the CHA, the CMA, and the HCSC. I soon discovered that the California Assembly health committee had scheduled an emergency meeting Saturday at the St. Francis Hotel in San Francisco and they wanted me present to testify on behalf of CHA. That a legislative committee would meet on a holiday and on Saturday afternoon indicated the issue's urgency.

I found out that unbeknownst to us at CHA, the CMA had commissioned a Dr. Blum, a PH.D. psychologist, to study the relationships at six hospitals between the medical staff, the governing board and the administration to determine the characteristics of these interrelationships that contributed to good patient care. Dr. Blum had submitted his report to CMA for review prior to its release with copies sent to several association leaders for comment.

The fly in the ointment, in the middle of the report, was a special section on different colored paper where Dr. Blum outlined what he described as examples of destructive-type rumors he found circulating in the hospitals he studied. Although he made no effort to verify the accuracy of the rumors, he considered them detrimental to good hospital operation and quality patient care. These unsubstantiated rumors were quite alarming. One rumor discussed a severe conflict between two surgeons in a hospital and claimed one even carried a pistol when in surgery. Another was about two doctors who had a fistfight in surgery. The third was a story of a physician in a community hospital who refused to treat an emergency patient who had Kaiser Permanente insurance and who directed the family to take her to a Kaiser facility some 50 miles away. Because of the delay the patient's condition had seriously deteriorated.

Unfortunately, one of those with an advance copy of the report leaked it to a reporter on the San Francisco *Call-Bulletin* who proceeded to write a series of articles based on the rumors. They began that Monday, and each day thereafter one more incident hit the pages. Apparently the reporter had made no effort to verify the incidents; however, being able to quote from an official CMA document gave the study credibility. As the week progressed the public outcry reached the Legislature which prompted the emergency meeting. There was strong indication that at least some of the legislators would attempt to use the publicity as a basis for establishing regulatory control over hospital medical staffs.

Getting to San Francisco was difficult that busy weekend. I let my family proceed to Washington, D.C. without me, and as no space was available to San Francisco, the CHA staff was able to get me on the Friday night red-eye into Los Angeles. There I was met early on Saturday morning at LAX by a HCSC staff member who handed me a copy of the report which, of course, I had never seen.

A local shuttle delivered me to San Francisco where I met with CHA and CMA staff, including Mr. Hassard, to discuss strategy. From New York I had suggested on the phone that since this appeared to be primarily a doctor problem I, as the representative of hospitals, should take the lead in recommending a positive solution, using the 1958 Guiding Principles for Hospitals as the model for responsive voluntary action to the Blum Report issues, with the CMA and CHA taking the leadership in developing a parallel set of policy statements on hospital/physician relationships. This suggestion was enthusiastically received, and that became my role.

Reading the Blum report on the ride to San Francisco from Los Angeles I found it actually to be an excellent piece of research, but it was totally destroyed by the eight-page rumor section. After a couple of hours sleep at the hotel, I then made the agreed-upon pitch to the committee. We distributed copies of the existing Guiding Principles for Hospitals to the committee and called their attention to the fact the document established a realistic pattern for the mutual responsibilities within the hospital structure that could be fleshed out and implemented on a statewide basis.

Fortuitously, there were some excellent legislators on the committee who had confidence in the integrity of CMA and CHA to follow through on our assurances. Mr. Hassard and the CMA physician representative committed CMA to development and implementation of the new Principles and included establishment of a CMA statewide survey program of hospital medical staffs, which would be in much greater depth than the existing Joint Commission on Accreditation of Hospitals surveys. Even though the committee accepted our proposals, it clearly indicated it would be watching to see how we performed.

A Joint Committee of CMA and CHA, which included Mr. Hassard and myself, went into immediate action to develop the new Guiding Principles for Physician/Hospital Relationships. This joint document, published in 1961, described the respective roles of the hospital governing body and the individual physician and spelled out in detail the entire peer review process for credentialing physicians to meet the quality of care commitment. It went on to establish a medical staff survey program to be coördinated with the Joint Commission on Accreditation of Hospitals' surveys thereby assuring that the two programs would complement each other to maximize the advantages of both. This was a unique program solely initiated in California.

The most important section of the new Principles was the addition of the CMA-CHA uniform code of hearing and appeal procedures for processing applications and renewals for medical staff membership plus the procedures for discipline. As finally approved by both organizations, this document carefully protected the rights of all parties and clearly spelled out the due process procedures to be followed. These have now become the national standard and in actual practice have substantially minimized the litigation over medical staff privileges in California and elsewhere.

Almost 40 years later, I feel the need to warn the healthcare provider community about the shift of power and authority within the medical community inherent in the movement to managed care. Through utilization controls and related activities the healthcare plans will exercise control over a patient's right to select physicians, both at the primary care level as gatekeepers and on to the specialists, as well as the hospital at which the patient is treated.

The whole issue of the rights of the patient as well as the rights of the physicians who are deselected will have to be revisited. Unless the healthcare community develops acceptable voluntary procedures such as those described here, the issues will be resolved by state and federal legislative action. Recent legislation mandating that a health plan accept any willing provider, or proposals to outlaw termination without cause provisions in physician contracts, are only the earliest manifestations of a need to resolve these critical questions about relationships.

We are finding that the medical staff/hospital governing board relationships can no longer play the role of assuring a balance between the rights of the patient and the individual healthcare provider in this new economic and legal environment. If the managed-care plans and the integrated medical groups are going to assume the power, they must maintain their public responsibility for social justice – not an easy role.

Hopefully, they can learn from our experience of the 1970s and 1980s. The solution of the healthcare cost problem cannot be resolved without full consideration of the people problems. As I have often said, "It is not enough to be right."

21

Hospital Planning & Regulation

Although the subjects of both hospital planning and hospital regulation are clearly interrelated and overlapping, in California they were treated separately at the early stages of legislative policy development.

Hospital planning was concerned primarily with making available to the public adequate and appropriately located healthcare facilities and programs to assure a broad spectrum of healthcare in what may be described as the institutional setting. On the other hand, hospital or healthcare regulation dealt with the issues of the cost and quality of healthcare and matters like state licensure of hospitals and other healthcare providers, including third party payors such as insurers, and availability and access to care.

However, in most major urban states various forms of regulation have been established to control cost and charging issues such as by insurance regulation or the establishment of hospital rate setting commissions. More recently the control and supervision of managed-care plans, such as HMOs and other groupings of providers or third party payors, has introduced a whole new area of state and federal regulation. In this chapter I treat the history of hospital planning in California that culminated in the passage of the certificate-of-need law.

The genesis for hospital planning and construction in California followed federal congressional action in 1944 to adopt what is generally known as the Hill-Burton law. This statute established a block grant program under which the states were assisted "in carrying out programs for construction and modernization of public or other nonprofit community hospitals and other medical facilities, as may be necessary, in conjunction with existing facilities to furnish adequate hospital, clinic, or similar services to all their people."

A state desiring to participate in the program was required to designate a single state agency as the sole entity for administering the plan. In addition, the state was required to establish an advisory council which would include representation from various groupings of healthcare providers, both public and private, as specified in the federal law. The state agency would create a statewide inventory of facilities as well as delineate the projected need for additional facilities, including not only acute-care hospital beds but also long-term-care beds, public health centers, outpatient and rehabilitation facilities.

Substantial detailed requirements and conditions were placed upon the process of individual applications for funds including hearings, all as a build-up to the state authority based upon the advisory council applications to set priorities and approved amounts. Approved amounts for an individual project could not exceed 33⅓ percent of the costs. The applicants were required to be nonprofit and to make provision for care of indigents. The state could also apply for the use of the federal allotment to cover up to 50 percent of its cost of administration of the program.

Needless to say, this was a honey pot of money that no state, particularly California, could overlook. Promptly at the 1947 legislative session the Legislature adopted the California Hospital Survey and Construction Act to implement the Hill-Burton program.

The hospital and medical environment during this period had been seriously impacted by the events of World War II. The war effort had caused an almost complete moratorium on hospital and related facility construction, contributing to the large backlog in needed hospital construction to serve the expanded population of the state. At the time the majority of the California hospitals were what we classify as not-for-profit community-based institutions, sponsored either by a church organization or an independent community league organized by physicians and the local business officials who were convinced that a local hospital was critical to the existence of a viable growing town or city.

This followed the pattern of the Eastern and Midwestern U.S. where the existence of philanthropy for the support of such facilities as schools, homes for the aged, orphanages and hospitals was considered a civic duty. Unfortunately, California, as a new, rapidly growing state, did not have the traditional public philanthropy support for the service commitments nor did it have the community resources accumulated as was the situation in the other parts of the country with older and more mature populations.

The situation in California was further complicated by existence of the district hospital law adopted in 1945, which authorized the creation of local hospital districts in essentially the same manner as other local governmental districts could be created, with authority to collect local taxes and be controlled by a local district hospital board elected by the voters in the district. Although district hospitals were primarily intended to help rural areas which had limited hospital facilities to finance and build a local hospital, many were created in suburban areas around big cities, particularly the San Francisco Bay area.

It should be noted that the law specifically prohibited the creation of district hospitals in Los Angeles County for many years as the result of opposition from the Catholic church, which wanted to protect its extensive hospital network throughout Southern California. The Hill-Burton funds became a key factor in the expansion of the number of district hospitals, which not only filled a local need but also could use the taxing and bonding authority to meet Hill-Burton's matching fund requirements.

The specialization of medical practice was also just at its beginning stages, so that general practice physicians were important sources of admissions to hospitals, and in many institutions they were in control of the medical staff.

When World War II ended, California experienced a tremendous influx of former G.I.s and their families. This growth caused a rapid expansion of complete new communities around the cities. Each community and its physicians felt the need for its own hospital as medical practice was centered around the local hospital. The hospital licensure law was designed to classify hospitals by size. If crossing the threshold number of 100 beds the law had substantial additional facility and service requirements; similarly, at 200 beds or more a morgue was dictated as well as other added facilities for a major hospital. There were also five classes of construction, going from wood frame and stucco to major steel and concrete facilities. Because of the immediate demand as well as cost, the tendency was to build either a 99- or 199-bed hospital.

Since the communities were so new, there was no tradition of wealth available from personal or corporate donors to fund tax-exempt entities to build new hospitals, so throughout this period new hospitals often were being created by the credit and financial support of physicians. However, these physicians were a varied group. Many were fine young people with excellent credentials, but others were substandard practitioners fleeing a community where they were no longer acceptable, and still others just wanted to make a fast buck. All of this became important as the state implemented its Hill-Burton program.

Another condition of federal approval required the state legislatures to create an advisory health council to be a key player in administering the program. The membership of this group was an important factor in maintaining both the effectiveness and integrity of the planning and allocation process. Fortunately, Gordon Cummings, a former executive in the Los Angeles County's department of health, was employed as the executive administrator of the plan. It was not only his knowledge and skills that contributed to its success, but also his absolute integrity. I am sure every imaginable form of pressure was put on Gordon during his many years of administering the program, but to my knowledge there was never a hint of scandal. Of course, throughout his tenure there were all forms of natural disasters – fire, flood and earthquakes – which obviously created special needs and shifts in priorities.

An inventory of existing facilities and a fluid five-year projection of future needs was created as part of the planning process. Unfortunately, this information created a road map for fast-moving entrepreneurs who could use the bed-shortage data as justification to secure debt financing of small (usually 99 beds or less) hospitals in one new community after another. This data also created some fierce competition and serious adversarial relationships among the established, nonprofit hospitals which sought to expand or protect their turf.

The underlying problem for the nonprofit sector projects was the time it took them to capitalize a project through existing organizations – such as the Catholic church or other church groups that stepped in. Thus the Lutheran Hospital Society in Los Angeles initially funded the Donald M. Sharp Memorial Hospital in San Diego, and the Hollywood Presbyterian Hospital funded Valley Presbyterian Hospital – a protracted project as compared to the time it took a for-profit developer to secure bond financing. Then as soon as a developer had financing and broke ground for a hospital, the bed-shortage data to support Hill-Burton funding would no longer be a factor and the nonprofit organizations would be left empty handed.

Thus in 1951 the California Hospital Association supported the introduction of an initiative on the ballot to amend (ACA 58) the State Constitution, (ARTICLE XVI, SECTION 3), to provide:

> Whenever federal funds are made available for the construction of hospital facilities by public agencies and nonprofit corporations organized to construct and maintain such facilities, nothing in this constitution shall prevent the Legislature from making state money available for the purpose, or from authorizing the use of such money for the construction of hospital facilities by nonprofit corporations organized to construct and maintain such facilities.

This initiative proposal passed and pursuant to this authorization the state Legislature provided state matching grants for county hospitals and hospital districts so that a qualifying project could receive a combined two-thirds grant. In 1955 after an extended four-years battle the state Legislature extended matching grants to nonprofit hospitals as well.

The struggles continued and finally by 1969 the state Legislature authorized another amendment to the state constitution adopting the California Health Facility Construction Loan Insurance Law, which was designed to provide, without cost to the state, an insurance program for hospital facility construction plus improvement and expansion loans for governmental and nonprofit organizations. This law prohibited provision of any insurance for a hospital or facility unless it had been approved through the statewide system of health facility planning. A similar program was adopted for mental health facilities in 1978 under the Community Mental Health Facilities Loan Insurance Law.

Thus the supply side of the hospital availability question was addressed, with emphasis placed on the role of the state and federal

Health Policy – The Hard Way

governments in financing construction and improvement of hospitals and related facilities. These programs were invaluable in supplying hospital facilities urgently needed to service the burgeoning population in California as well as to handle the dramatic changes in how medicine was practiced, particularly in surgery.

At the time we did not anticipate how the momentum created would lead to an over-expansion of hospital facilities. Now with the shift to outpatient services and the pressure on occupancy created by the development of managed-care plans, this over-capacity has become increasingly serious. With the rapid expansion of proprietary hospital facilities in certain areas of the state, often encouraged by the state plan, leadership in the health field became increasingly concerned about the potential for excess capacity since there was no overall planning as to efficient use of our healthcare resources.

Governor Pat Brown in 1960 created what was known as the Governor's Committee on Medical Aid and Health with Roger O. Egeberg, M.D., medical director of Los Angeles County's department of charities, as the chair. The committee of 19 members was broad based and broke up into a series of task forces. My personal role while serving on several of the task forces, was to work with the hospital leaders in making the report a meaningful guideline for the future development of the healthcare system, including its role and finances for the future.

One statement in the introduction to the report was particularly important:

> In the past 30 years, the concept of planning to many people has come to mean, centralized power, strong government control and federal interference in local affairs. The Committee wishes to stress a different meaning of planning. The recommendations, on the whole, are aimed at decentralization. Planning should involve more voluntary coöperation at the community level, where desire to help the aged, indigent sick and the crippled is often born.

The Committee is confident that, presented with the facts properly developed, people will come to the right decisions. Armed with knowledge they will reject arbitrary authority.

This was a strong statement of the basic philosophy of those representing the healthcare industry, including both hospitals and medicine. The report was designed to project the needs for healthcare for the following 15 years and carefully documented the trends and cost of satisfying these needs. It then stated:

The Committee urges that councils be set up in the various regions of the State (representing health professions, health facilities, and the public) for the purpose of planning and coördinating the health services of their own communities. A primary responsibility of these councils would be to develop plans for better location of new hospitals and related facilities.

Significantly, the committee's recommendation was for voluntary action and did not include any guidance for a planning authority with the right to say yes or no. I cannot emphasize too much how we truly believed we should and could do the job on a voluntary basis – but how wrong we were.

At that time it was the role of Chuck Forbes and myself to lobby the 1961 Legislature to implement these recommendations. This was one whale of a fight as there were forces in the Legislature who wanted to put stronger teeth in the proposed planning legislation that the CHA caused to be introduced. It came to a point where, as the result of amendments adopted by the legislative committees, particularly in the Senate, we were in the awkward position of opposing our own legislation. However, ultimately the Legislature enacted a planning bill acceptable to the CHA and CMA. The bill authorized the Advisory Hospital Council to establish two planning regions, one in each of the metropolitan areas of San Francisco and Los Angeles, with a board of ten members each. The goal of this legislation was to encourage a voluntary planning process without resort to a public utility concept.

Each local committee was directed to

(a) review information on utilization of hospitals, related community health facilities, and health services;
(b) develop principles and standards of community need to guide hospitals, related community health facilities and health services in meeting needs of the public;
(c) conduct public meetings in which professional groups and consumer groups will be encouraged to participate.

The local hospital committees were required to report to the Legislature at the beginning of the 1963 legislative session. The act would sunset 90 days after the close of the 1963 session. At its 1963 legislative session the Legislature authorized creation of hospital planning regions in the San Diego area and the South San Joaquin Valley area and put a new deadline for reports and put off the sunsetting of the act until 1965. At the 1965 session of the Legislature the sunsetting deadline was again extended and the voluntary planning effort was made statewide.

These legislative actions brought about immediate action to create the local voluntary planning committees. Until the 1969 Legislature these planning committees had no teeth in their recommendations. Basically the concept was that by having the voluntary planning process, any developer of a hospital facility project would want the blessing of the local planning committee as evidence of community support and need, which in turn would affect the developer's ability to raise financing or community capital support. Also, it avoided the constitutional issues of due process and equal protection.

Perhaps we were naïve, but we believed the voluntary process would work. However, we received a dose of reality when we found that there was very little voluntary financial support from the business community to maintain the process. We had been convinced that the business community, with its expressed concern for healthcare costs, would pitch in to help. Except for a few insurance companies and some minimum help from the banks the effort was primarily supported by the healthcare providers.

When Congress passed the Medicare and Medicaid laws in 1965, thereby financing a major expanded demand for all types of health services, there was a new surge of hospital construction projects, many of which completely ignored the voluntary planning process and were able to successfully finance their capital projects. As a result there developed an increased level of frustration by the hospital community at the failure of the voluntary planning process.

In 1967 the California Hospital Association board of trustees reversed its position and supported legislation that would make the planning process mandatory – with teeth. It was my role as legal counsel to CHA along with Gordon Cummings, executive of the Advisory Hospital Council, to present the proposed legislation to the Assembly's committee on public health. We knew it would be a tough battle because the hospital industry was badly split on this change in policy.

There was especially strong opposition by the East Bay hospitals in the north where Kaiser Permanente went all out in opposition because of its fear that such legislation would be used to limit its expansion, which relied heavily on the construction of new hospitals. The CMA was also in opposition on the philosophical ground that governmental control over healthcare was bad. Gordon and I appeared and presented our case to the committee and, as I now recall, we got two votes and were torn to pieces by committee members. That was one of my worst defeats in the legislative process.

However, by 1969 the continued proliferation of hospital construction finally mobilized the hospital industry. Even the physician community realized that something more drastic had to be done, so we went back to the drawing boards to develop some compromise legislation. The act adopted by the Legislature required that no license or construction permits should be issued without approval from the respective voluntary health planning agency. The statute (SECTIONS 438.6, 439.7, H & S, JANUARY 1, 1976) established the procedure to be followed by the voluntary health planning agencies, including a specified appellate procedure.

The penalty provision that was included required a promoter of a new or expanded facility either to obtain approval of a project or before it could apply for a license be required to delay for twelve months from the date of denial of the application for approval. All governmental agencies were required to take into consideration the findings and actions of the planning agency to the fullest extent legally permitted. In other words, this did not mean an absolute "no" but a substantial delay before proceeding with a project.

Although this approach was partially successful in eliminating certain underfinanced projects, there were many others that simply waited out the time period and proceeded. As a result, we went back to the Legislature with a request for a strong certificate of need law. The Legislature adopted an urgency bill effective September 9, 1976, requiring a certificate of need for all new construction and all increase in capacity or conversion of existing facilities of a capital cost in excess of $150,000 with the same $150,000 limit on the purchase or lease of diagnostic or therapeutic equipment. This affected all hospitals and was a major jolt to those planning expansion or additional costly services.

The procedures required of the planning agencies were substantially upgraded and the battle lines were drawn in many communities as former friends lined up to support or oppose specific projects. A side effect was to increase substantially the number of lawyers and consultants in the adversary process. Historically, the hospital community in Southern California had been a coöperative and friendly environment, but with certificate of need and the conflicts of interests that developed the atmosphere changed.

By 1979 the number of hospital projects had been substantially reduced. To some degree this was achieved by clauses in the 1976 legislation which transferred the ultimate decision on a project to the state's Department of Health advisory health council, thereby reducing the authority of the area health planning agencies to a solely advisory capacity. Thus ended our experiment with voluntary planning and the use of local voluntary boards as decision makers.

Looking back at our experiments with a variety of voluntary efforts over the years—some very successful, some not—I can see that when we were successful two key elements were invariably present: 1) a shared sense of mutual long-term benefit among the participants, and 2) a certain amount of benevolent dictatorship to jump-start the process.

Foretelling the future was the special treatment enacted for HMO healthcare facilities in the planning process. In 1979 the Legislature provided specific exemption for HMO projects so they could be judged upon the needs of their own members. Since this was during a major expansion of the Kaiser Permanente Plan it was critical to their program. After that, nearly every session of the Legislature added new exemptions to the planning law until finally at the 1984 session the Legislature suspended the entire certificate of need program effective January 1, 1987, thus ending the entire effort at health facility planning.

The present problem is how to deal with the existing overexpansion of hospital facilities as marketplace forces and medical practice changes have cut the actual average occupancy of hospitals statewide to approximately 50 percent against the accepted optimal efficiency of approximately 80 percent. Unfortunately, with marketplace competition the hospitals most likely to fail are the urban centers with a high ratio of medically indigent patients. Without our planning effort this situation would have been much worse.

We have found that one of the hardest things to do is to kill a hospital – even one that is failing economically. As long as that facility exists in a community there is some group – often a circle of physicians – who will attempt to keep it open. They are encouraged in these efforts by those entities that hold the debt which is generally in place, and who experience a severe loss if the hospital is closed. Since each hospital develops its own constituency in the community, there are those who fight for its survival even though that hospital is redundant.

As the demand for inpatient care shrinks, all of the hospitals in the area suffer as they compete for the reducing market shares. As a practical matter, the current financial success of managed-care insurance plans has been based upon the plans' ability to play one hospital off against the other by engaging in selective contracting. Even Blue Cross that was founded by the hospital industry on the basic philosophy of contracting with every qualified hospital has abandoned its original concept.

The solution to the over-capacity problem is complicated by a revival of strict antitrust enforcement, making it difficult for a group of hospitals to combine to eliminate one or more of their group. From time to time I have suggested it might be in the best interest of government and other major purchasers of hospital services to legislate what I call a reverse Hill-Burton program under which funds would be made available to acquire redundant hospitals and either scrap them or convert them to other community uses such as long-term care or even housing for the elderly or homeless.

Whenever I hear politicians criticize the healthcare industry for its overexpansion, I can only respond that we certainly tried to do the right thing.

❦ The California Hospital Disclosure Act

Paralleling the legislative action on hospital construction, a second phase of control over hospitals in California was the evolution of the California Hospital Disclosure Act of 1971, as well as other efforts to control healthcare costs.

Costs have always been a critical issue for hospitals in both the public relations and the legislative arenas. Although health insurance alleviated the problem for many individuals, the cost of health insurance itself became an issue for employers as well as individuals. This situation was aggravated in Southern California where employment has been primarily by small employers rather than by the big industrial firms as is true in many parts of the country where major employers have comprehensive health insurance fringe benefits as part of their employee benefit programs. In California, and particularly Southern California, more than half of the small employers do not provide health insurance for their employees because, they say, of the costs.

Hospital leaders like Sam Tibbitts, John Brewer and Steve Gamble were particularly sensitive to the issue of hospital costs and developed such programs as the Commission For Administrative Services to Hospitals (CASH) in 1963 to bring management effectiveness into the day-to-day hospital operating activities. Among the other activities were the various "Guiding Principles" which they developed – for hospital planning, for personnel relations, and the general one for hospitals, discussed in depth in chapter eight of this volume.

In other parts of the country, particularly the urban Eastern states, there developed in the late '60s a pattern of legislative action to control hospital costs by requiring that state commissions annually approve individual hospital budgets and the charge schedules as a condition of their licensure. This has been loosely described as the public utility approach to controlling hospital costs.

In the 1970s the decision as to whether the California Hospital Association would support the creation of such a state commission became a hot issue. The battle was aligned between two strong and articulate leaders, Gordon Cummings, with his background in the

Hill-Burton program advocating state controls, and Sam Tibbitts, the leader of a marketplace solution with no mandatory state budget controls over individual hospitals. Both argued from a position that theirs would be in the long run in the best interest of both patients and hospitals. To buttress their case they each had a litany of success and horror stories from our Eastern peers.

Fortunately, at that time Emery (Soap) Dowell was in charge of government relations (lobbying) for the CHA. Before coming to the CHA he had been a lobbyist for the Pacific Gas and Electric Company, the major public utility in northern California. He was intimately familiar with the pros and cons of industry regulation. At his suggestion, Professor Morrissey from the faculty at the University of California and also a former member of the California Public Utilities Commission was employed by the CHA board to consider the possible impact on hospitals of industry-wide regulation along the lines of a public utility.

Professor Morrissey's resulting report was very significant and helpful in the ongoing debate. He gave us an historical perspective to the issues, pointing out that one of the patterns followed by industries, such as the telephone companies and other public utilities, was to create their own regulatory scheme and then politically control it, at least for the start-up period. Sooner or later there would be a public reaction, such as occurred to the railroad industry during the Hiram Johnson days.

In his view Professor Morrissey found the closest prototype for the hospital industry to be the trucking industry. Though having many elements of an essential public service, trucking was made up of a large number of small business units which were highly competitive in local markets. The regulation of trucking by both the state and federal governments not only put caps on charges but also controlled competition to assure the survival of the small independent operators. Unfortunately, I can no longer find a copy of this report when it would once again be timely as the hospital industry considers the advisability of going the public utility approach to deal with the problems of overcapacity and ruthless competition.

In the late 1960s and early 1970s, John Brewer, CEO of the Hospital Council, used a technique nicknamed the "Marching and Chowder Society". This consisted of the elected officers of the council plus five or six senior statespersons in the industry who would go on a weekend retreat to the Santa Barbara Biltmore Hotel to discuss industry problems and hopefully develop policy recommendations for the HCSC board of directors. These were excellent meetings and productive. One was scheduled in late 1970 to consider the issue of state regulation of hospitals.

As legal counsel to the council I attended these meetings as an active participant. I left late Friday afternoon to drive up alone to the 1970 meeting, deeply troubled by the divisiveness of the issue to the industry and the need to come up with a consensus solution before one was imposed on us by the Legislature. There bills were being introduced to establish state control over both budgeting and pricing by hospitals. About two-thirds of the way up to the meeting, going by the location where a Japanese submarine was supposed to have lobbed a couple of shells onto the bluffs overlooking the highway shortly after Pearl Harbor, the thought came to me that perhaps an acceptable compromise for the industry would be to take what is known in legal circles as the S.E.C. approach to industry regulation.

Under this strategy any business seeking to issue major public financing offerings is required to make a full disclosure of the financial status of the offering company. The S.E.C. does not take a position on the advisability of the proposed security, but it does require that the public have access to the information on which to make a judgment and to assure that the information is complete and understandable.

Arriving at the Santa Barbara meeting I proposed this concept for the hospital industry, pointing out that one of the major problems facing the industry was a lack of credibility with the public on its internal operations. At that time few hospitals published or released their internal financial reports and many of them did not require complete annual CPA audits. Probably as a result of their so-called charitable status, hospitals kept their finances confidential. They felt that they were something special and not subject to public scrutiny.

It also seemed to me that the availability of such industry-wide financial data would be useful to the individual hospitals in doing effective planning and making critical management decisions as this data was analyzed.

After a heated debate the concept was accepted and recommended to both the HCSC and the CHA boards for 1971 legislative action. Our office was directed to prepare the proposed legislation which was done forthwith, passed and approved by Governor Ronald Reagan on October 26, 1971. The objectives of the law were to:

1. Encourage economy and efficiency in the provision of healthcare services.
2. Enable public agencies to make informed decisions in purchasing and administering publicly-financed healthcare.
3. Encourage organizations providing hospital insurance to take into account financial information provided to the hospital commission created by the act in establishing reimbursement rates.
4. Assist in planning and designing improved means of providing healthcare.
5. Stabilize hospital costs through the efforts of public scrutiny of cost factors.
6. Eliminate or reduce budget crises in public programs by providing accurate information to improve budget planning.
7. Create a large body of reliable information for research into the economics of healthcare.

The act established a seven-member commission, three of

whom were representatives of the general public, all appointed by the governor. The commission with the use of a ten-member advisory council, was directed to design a uniform accounting system, including (1) detailed assets, liabilities and net worth, (2) a statement of income, expenses and operating surplus, (3) a statement detailing the source and application of funds, (4) a statement of expenditures to include allocations to departments, and (5) a statistical report sufficiently detailed to identify costs related to categories, types or units of hospital care services delivered to patients.

All reports were to be open to public inspection. The filing of the report was a condition of licensure and the commission had the right to audit for accuracy and completeness. The program was financed by an annual fee up to 0.02 percent of each hospital's gross operating cost of the provision of healthcare services.

While the CHA board continues to oppose any legislative action to declare hospitals to be public utilities or to establish a rate and budget control program, the data collection function has been expanded to include an annual hospital discharge abstract date record to provide an important source of data on information from patients' records as to diagnosis, treatment, total charges and expected source of payment. The financial data also has been expanded and now requires summary quarterly reports. For 1993 and thereafter the Legislature mandated that the health facilities file information in the form of a risk-adjusted report on patient outcomes and then required that the agency publish annual reports comparing individual hospital results – a highly controversial subject.

In 1984 the Legislature combined the functions of the California Health Facilities Commission and the State Advisory Health Council into a single California Health Policy and Data Advisory Commission of eleven members. With the rapid expansion into managed care we can expect that the breadth and sophistication of the reports will continue to be emphasized as the public and third-party payors seek valid report cards on individual healthcare providers and provider organizations.

At least up to now the concept of disclosure as a substitute for direct regulation appears to be a success. Certainly the move from inpatient to outpatient care and the expansion of integrated care has been much easier as healthcare providers have been able to experiment with new organizational forms with a minimum of direct governmental intrusion in the process of operating healthcare facilities.

One of the questions that has always been in the thinking of our healthcare leaders is how much risk there is in placing control of the flow of sensitive information and data into the hands of a government bureaucracy. The experience at both the federal level and the state level has indicated the abuse or danger comes from the way in which the government agency releases raw data without adequate refinement or interpretation so that individual providers may be unfairly injured. The physician community is particularly sensitive to this issue as outcome data is released in the form of report cards. Looking to the future it is clear that in the whole battle over the quality of care, those issues relating to the financial incentives of managed care will be of great concern to both community activists and healthcare providers.

In this regard it is useful to recall the experience of CHA and CMA in the 1970s when Sam Tibbitts promoted the concept that healthcare providers, both physicians and hospitals, should control the database. Sam led the charge for a voluntary effort by creating the California Health Data Corporation, jointly controlled by CHA and CMA, and with Sister Jane Frances as the chairperson, with a goal to collect and professionally evaluate healthcare data.

Much effort went into this endeavor, and for a period it was quite successful. However, lacking the mandate of licensure or some other enforcement mechanism, it gradually deteriorated through lack of coöperation by the healthcare providers and was abandoned. Like voluntary planning it was impossible to move a giant industry without some form of compulsion.

In this context I am reminded of a speech I gave to one of the annual leadership conferences conducted jointly by CHA and the three hospital councils as a forum for developing industry policy positions on the critical issues of the day. In the mid-1970s, after the adoption of the Hospital Disclosure Act and the dissipation of the threat of a state public utility approach for hospitals, I was asked to discuss the potentials of marketplace competition.

My theme was that for a variety of reasons most hospital CEOs were convinced that in competition based on quality and cost, their own hospital would be a winner. However, I suggested that in reality it was possible there would be no winners, but all could be losers. A very quiet audience listened as I explained my reasoning. I pointed out that each individual hospital had a high capital cost that was substantially inflexible and needed just to keep its doors open. Once the capital was committed there was no way to withdraw the capital or reduce the capital cost (overhead) except by allowing the structure to deteriorate.

In the real world there was a finite demand or market share and each hospital could expand in a mature market only at the expense of its neighbors. However, since hospitals are essentially single-purpose structures, a hospital that is threatened with loss of market share is forced to reduce prices or engage in promotions to the medical community. Consequently, it is the weak hospital, not the strong hospital, that sets the local quality standard and cost of care. When there is substantial excess of capacity, as has existed since the early 1980s, to kill an existing hospital and redirect its market share is a long and traumatic experience that rarely happens. Even though the working capital of an organization may be exhausted, a new sponsor will take over with new incentives to the physician community and fight for the shrinking market share.

This is important because the optimal inpatient occupancy for a hospital is about 80 percent. When it drops into the 60 percent area, the cash flow is periled, even though it can continue to operate by exhausting its fixed capital assets. Of equal importance is that as the total market share is reduced by various mechanisms, such as utilization review and shortened length of hospital days, all hospitals suffer.

This is where I first publicly suggested that what we needed was a reverse Hill-Burton program under which the federal and state governments, jointly with the private sector, would finance a program to take selected hospitals totally out of the market. Such a cost could be justified because the closer the surviving hospitals approached optimal utilization the more likelihood that their individual finances and quality of care would substantially improve. Furthermore, the direct participation of the government in this process was necessary to eliminate the antitrust problems that could arise if the hospitals combined to initiate such a process.

I still encounter those who were present at that session who come up and remind me of that speech. The potential of a reverse Hill-Burton plan is still a viable solution now, as the industry suffers both the economic and public relations damage from overcapacity.

With the present reduction of inpatient occupancy to an average of 50 percent and the continued switch from inpatient to outpatient care and surgery, the need for some such solution is obvious. At the same time there is a need for restructuring the high cost specialty services being imposed by the managed-care movement to primary care physician control and risk assumption. Although the present healthcare systems have enjoyed major savings in cost by central purchasing and other operational efficiencies inherent in size, the truly major cost savings of total integration are not available because usually a system includes facilities spread over a wide geographic area rather than being clustered. The role of the physicians is critical to such an evolution as they also must cluster.

This clustering of competing healthcare facilities is an extremely difficult task. In the early 1980s Hank Dunlap, then CEO at Childrens Hospital, Los Angeles, asked me to lead a task force on behalf of a group of downtown Los Angeles hospitals that would explore restructuring the central Los Angeles hospitals around their relationships with the University of Southern California School of Medicine.

At the time the threat of antitrust prosecution was not nearly as great as it is now and we therefore felt we would be able to deal with collaboration around a teaching setting. Thus we created a blue ribbon planning committee comprising the chief of staff and the chair of the governing boards of each of the downtown hospitals plus the USC medical school. We met every month for over a year. Because of the physician involvement we had to gather in the early morning hours – a necessary bore to assure their participation.

Our goal was to design a comprehensive restructuring of the entire healthcare delivery system for downtown Los Angeles, with each hospital being assigned its areas of excellence and providing universal access to the facilities by all physicians, all under the leadership of the USC School of Medicine.

When we were in substantial agreement and were in the process of preparing our final report and recommendations to the ten healthcare entities that participated, we received a communication from the chair of the board of the Hospital of the Good Samaritan stating that because of medical staff opposition to the pending recommendations, the hospital was withdrawing from the project or any implementation to the report.

Due to the vital role played by the Hospital of the Good Samaritan to the whole fabric of the report, this was a fatal blow and further work on the report ceased. The importance of the Good Sam participation arose from the fact that basic to the restructuring concept was the substantial conversion of Good Sam to be the principal base for the private practice of the USC School of Medicine full-time teaching faculty. It was agreed by the task force that the existence of readily available hospital privileges for their private practice was an essential component to the ability of the medical school to attract highly qualified faculty.

Because of its physical location and the nature of its practice it was our belief that Good Sam was ideally suited to perform this role, with the other hospitals sharing allocated departmental responsibilities for faculty in other key specialties. However, the medical staff of the Good Sam was particularly sensitive to the town and gown syndrome. They did not want to compete with the USC faculty for the use of hospital facilities and were concerned about the potential impact on their individual referral base.

Every one of the downtown hospitals is struggling to find its proper role. Now there is serious discussion by healthcare leaders in this community that, as a result of the current budget crisis for the county and the cutback on available county healthcare services, there again needs to be an objective high-powered study to devise a restructuring of both the private sector and the public health resources in a way that will use these resources more efficiently in a public-private partnership approach, using the medical schools as a focal point to preserve the essential educational component to the Los Angeles area health system.

If such a study occurs, it must not only deal with the issue of assuring care to the Medicare and the MediCal patients but also the several million uninsured in this county at the same time it proposes to resolve the overriding problem of excess in patient bed capacity and the continued shrinking of inpatient utilization for a variety of reasons.

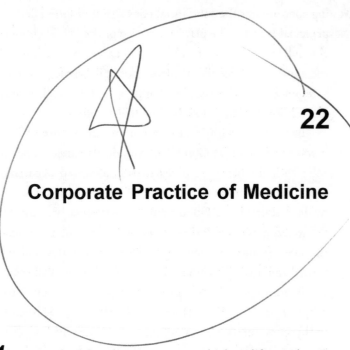

22

Corporate Practice of Medicine

The major health policy issue over which California hospitals and organized medicine have had an emotional running disagreement for six decades is the legal prohibition against the corporate practice of medicine as stated in the case of *Pacific Employers Ins. Co. v. Carpenter*, 10 CAL. APP. 2D 592 (1935):

> Under the foregoing authorities it is clearly declared unlawful for a corporation to indirectly practice any of said professions for profit by engaging professional men to perform professional services for those with whom the corporation contracts to furnish such services. In other words, said authorities declare that said professions are not open to commercial exploitation as it is said to be against public policy to permit a 'middleman' to intervene for profit in establishing the professional relationships between the members of said professions and the members of the public.

To the leadership of organized medicine this is a do-or-die issue with both economic and ethical implications that make it nonnegotiable. On the other hand, hospital leadership has found the concept an unfortunate barrier to the solution of many problems involving all phases of healthcare, including quality, access and cost. Besides, they find it totally irrational. Still the policy of CHA as the legislative policy body for hospitals has been to avoid challenging the CMA on the issue on two basic grounds: First, the adverse impact on many other issues upon which the CMA and CHA must work together would be so great that it is not worth the battle; and second, the commitment of CMA is so great that it would expend whatever resources were necessary to defeat a repeal – and would probably win the battle. However, it is also anticipated that at some time the issue will be resolved by federal preëmption or a court decision that the corporate-practice-of-medicine prohibition is unconstitutional.

This is an issue that is almost peculiar to California, since it is one of only four states where the specific prohibition exists. My own personal advice to the CHA over these many years has been that it is not in the best interest of hospitals to challenge the CMA on the issue but that at some point it will resolve itself.

In the meantime the actual application of legal doctrine is gradually being whittled down by creative solutions, or being substantially ignored, as both the CMA and the office of the attorney general have been reluctant to raise a confrontation by way of enforcement. On the other hand, hospital and healthcare attorneys cannot ignore the issue in giving written legal advice or opinion on major transactions on the utilization of physician services. Recently the issue has been manifest in the creation of various healthcare entities involved in managed care, whether it be HMOs, PPOs or integrated medical group providers in which the use of employed physicians has a major potential. With the over supply of licensed physicians and the shrinking of fee-for-service medicine the pressure on the individual physician to consider the security of employment will increase the pressure for change.

My first experience with this issue came soon after I began the practice of law and was assigned the responsibility of representing hospitals negotiating arrangements between them and what was described as hospital-based physicians – generally radiologists or pathologists in the early days, but later anesthesiologists and emergency care physicians. Not only was the availability of these physicians absolutely necessary for the operation of a hospital, but they were members of strongly organized specialty societies whose members had every intention of preserving their legal and professional prerogatives aggressively, both within the political structure of the CMA and county medical societies and within each individual medical staff. Much of their activity came close to violating antitrust principles.

The challenge was to develop creative arrangements that would not violate the law on corporate practice but that would also assure the hospital of its fair share of the patient charge to cover its direct costs and overhead and would contribute to a hospital's discretionary income for capital and program purposes. The no-no was anything that smacked of fee-splitting while endeavoring to maximize a fair return to all parties.

There were many ancillary issues, such as the right of the hospital-based physician to maintain a private office – perhaps across the street from the hospital – and compete directly with the hospital by creaming off the pay patients while dumping the non-pay patients on the hospital. Then there was the selection and compensation of ancillary personnel. Doctors had a bias for paying their personnel at a higher rate than the other hospital personnel. This could be exceedingly disruptive to hospital policy. Other issues concerned the management of the office functions, particularly the billing of patients. Above all else, the hospital-based doctors did not want to submit and process separate bills as theirs would be the last ones paid.

Ritz Heerman, superintendent of the California Hospital in

Los Angeles, had worked out a creative concept to avoid the issue of fee-splitting which we described as the "modified gross arrangement". Under these terms the hospital would be reimbursed from the fee pool for all its direct costs in connection with the department, including personnel, supplies and use of equipment and space, and then would receive a percentage of the balance for its overhead, parking and other costs. This placed the physician and hospital on the same side of the fence for keeping down the controllable costs such as supplies and personnel – and both parties profited from the volume in the department.

Taking the Ritz Heerman concept to a joint committee of the CMA and CHA we developed a series of model agreements for each professional group – which became the statewide pattern. However, one feature of the contract concerned an exclusive arrangement with the physician. From the hospital point of view it was critical to have one individual or group responsible for 24-hour coverage and to assure quality of service.

This provision then became a legal battleground whenever an individual physician would drop out of the group and still want to maintain medical staff privileges and treat or diagnose patients utilizing the hospital facilities. A whole series of lawsuits developed, led by the case of *Blank v. Palo Alto Stanford Hospital*, 234 CAL. APP. 2D 377 (1965), challenging the exclusive control for radiology at the Palo Alto Stanford Hospital. It was my role to appear as an expert witness before the trial court and explain the background of the model agreements. Fortunately, the agreement was upheld as legal and the model agreements continue in place and will continue to do so until such time as the corporate practice of medicine issue is finally resolved.

During the early days after developing the model agreements I was asked to appear before the membership of the Los Angeles County Medical Association to explain them. I will always remember being introduced as "the man you love to hate."

As a practical matter the biggest blow to the corporate practice of medicine prohibition in California was adoption of the professional corporation law, which in effect permitted physicians to incorporate and, as such, to practice medicine in the corporate form and for its professional corporation to employ physicians. In other words it is all right for physicians to exploit each other. This mechanism has been utilized by managed-care entities as well as academic practice plans in providing the professional component of their operations.

The statutory prohibition against the corporate practice of medicine has another impact not generally understood by many physicians: it effectively denies the right of physicians on a medical staff to organize themselves as a labor union with all of the protections available under the National Labor Relations Act. This is becoming increasingly onerous to physician groups who seek better protection from managed-care companies bent on aggressively controlling and limiting physician fees. The physicians are frustrated by antitrust laws that limit their ability to organize group boycotts and other tactics available to labor unions.

Personally, I have always been of the opinion that the statute is unconstitutional under the California constitution as an unjustified interference with the freedom to pursue what is otherwise a legal business relationship. As a practical matter it will probably be eliminated by federal preëmption as it nearly was under various amendments proposed in the aborted healthcare reform plan of 1994 favored by Hillary Clinton.

23

National Health Foundation

In 1973 Steve Gamble and I were discussing the need for the Hospital Council of Southern California to have a tax-exempt entity for the purposes of soliciting and receiving grants for research and educational programs on healthcare in the council area. The council itself, as a trade association, did not qualify for such purposes, and there was no comparable entity in Southern California dedicated to healthcare problems. Not only was there a perceived need but it also appeared that in view of the leadership role of Southern California healthcare providers such an entity would attract outside foundation support.

We therefore proceeded to organize a not-for-profit foundation named The Hospital Educational Foundation of Southern California, a 501(C)(3) tax-exempt public benefit corporation. The members of the executive committee of the Hospital Council constituted the corporation members of the new entity. They, in turn, elected the board of trustees with an authorized number of from seven to twenty-one, at least two being members of the board of directors of the Hospital Council of Southern California, together with the president of the HCSC. The remaining members were selected from the general community. Even though the entity had strong ties with the HCSC it had substantial independence in order to attract leadership from beyond the hospital field.

We had great expectations for the future role of the foundation, but it initially progressed slowly. It did, however, receive a few grants for special projects. Its most successful project in its early years was to take over operation of the Hall of Health at the Museum of Science and Industry, located on the grounds of the Los Angeles Coliseum in South Central Los Angeles. This exhibit, originally organized by the Los Angeles County Medical Association, provided displays on health education planned primarily for school children but also open to adults. At this juncture the exhibit was rather musty and needed substantial upgrading and restoration. The foundation, using hospital contributions plus a major grant from Arco, transformed the Hall of Health into a state-of-the-art interactive exhibit with strong emphasis on health preservation, including innovative exhibits on the potential hazards of alcohol and drug abuse.

As time passed it became increasingly apparent that the name Hospital Educational Foundation of Southern California did not adequately identify the true nature and program of the entity. Because of the rapid proliferation of acronyms and names it was difficult to identify a new moniker not already used by someone else. Somehow we landed on "National Health Foundation" and in 1990 this new name, which more clearly indicates its scope and mission, was adopted.

Not until Ms. Rita Moya became its president and CEO in 1990 did the foundation begin to achieve its objective, which Steve Gamble described as being the conscience of Southern California's hospitals. Under Rita's leadership the foundation has become a significant factor in identifying major problems of healthcare access and then designing, funding and implementing solutions. This has involved a process of action research where the foundation identified critical problems, then raised seed money to produce a specific plan of action, which in turn was presented to major funding sources for purposes of implementing a solution.

The foundation's goal for such projects was that they either complete their objectives in the project's lifetime or, in the alternative, become self-sustaining. Recently, increased emphasis has been on the use of high technology to improve healthcare efficiency through intercommunication and data coördination for problem solving, coupled with better use of both public and private resources during a time of shrinking budgets and increased need for health services for the uninsured and underinsured.

Examples of the foundation's success in these areas include the AIM Project for access to prenatal and postnatal care for unsponsored infants and mothers through the creation of eight self-supporting clinics by separate agencies. These have filled a growing gap in the availability of such services with the shrinkage of the healthcare system, both public and private, in the Los Angeles area. A unique feature of this project has been the utilization of an intensive community outreach program to recruit the mothers into the network through use of trained outreach workers based in local churches or other community entities. Experience has shown that these mothers had to be recruited for care. The project, expanded into pediatric care, is now on a self-sustaining basis.

Another venture for the foundation was the re-engineering of the State Poison Control Network into a single effective cost-saving statewide center. This replaced six competing centers which were in jeopardy due to budget cuts. The use of high tech communication equipment made this possible and it became a prototype for adoption by centers nationwide.

A major concern for the foundation has been identifying and

strengthening the community-based free or part-pay clinics as a critical safety network resource for indigent patients. This has become a critical project as the county has faced major budget cuts with the consequent need to move from inpatient care to outpatient provisions. Not only has this clinic association been organized under NHF guidance, but also it now has its own dedicated staff. At the same time, the National Health Foundation actively recruited major providers such as managed-care plans and hospitals to act as partners for specific clinics. The partners provide money and equipment as well as people to assist these clinics in improving their operating efficiency and in expanding their needed programs. Recently, concentration has been on improving data management and communication to use these resources more effectively.

The foundation has also created what has been called the L.A. Model—a comprehensive interactive database for healthcare planning for inpatient and emergency care as well as outpatient care. Eventually this tool will include mental health and overall public health and will be made available to all interested parties in both the public and private sectors.

NHF's creation of the Health Data Information Corporation as a free-standing, self-supporting statewide entity for the total integration of the data systems for patient care, patient-care financing and claims processing is a major breakthrough in quality and cost-effective healthcare data management. Jointly sponsored and controlled by healthcare providers and information technology resources, this project under way has almost unlimited potential, for it can help assure better quality of care as well as major cost saving by integrating the total patient record for all providers and funders of care.

Working with the Health 4 L.A. has been a project initiated by the foundation in collaboration with the Los Angeles Chamber of Commerce. Health 4 L.A. is developing a health insurance product that emphasizes outpatient care with minimum costs to reach a critical uninsured market with emphasis on the care of children and a need to utilize the resources of the private physicians and clinics in the place of costly emergency-room visits.

The foundation also continues to serve as a forum for leaders of healthcare providers, managed-care plans and government sources in a problem-solving mode. Recently the foundation initiated a program to create a five million dollar endowment by the year 2000. The income of this will be used as seed money – perhaps better described as venture capital – to identify, organize and fund projects which will meet patient needs not otherwise helped by existing programs. The endowment will also assure the ability of the foundation to maintain a core staff and resources to respond rapidly to critical community health needs.

In many respects my continued association with this organization and the leadership it has recruited has been one of the most gratifying experiences of my long years in the field of hospital policy. It has clearly been people-motivated, which is the heart of healthcare. As the healthcare system continues to be reorganized and downsized, the need for innovative solutions on an action basis, utilizing both public and private resources, will become increasingly important.

24

Healthcare Reform Proposal

As the 1992 presidential election process developed, it became increasingly apparent that again the potential of a national action on healthcare reform was a reality. Steve Gamble and I had extended discussions on how this change could be approached in a constructive manner to avoid the failures of previous efforts. Initially we had certain important assumptions based on our experience in prior reform efforts. These were:

1. Healthcare reform can only be accomplished if there is a national recognition of a crisis in the cost and availability of healthcare which impacts all elements of society. With anything less than that the cause is doomed to failure. It was our conclusion that such an occasion was rapidly emerging and that the next newly elected president, Republican or Democrat, would, during a honeymoon period immediately following the 1992 election, have an opportunity to successfully lead such a movement. In other words, things were rapidly getting bad enough to force action but, more importantly, if the window of opportunity was not seized the chance would not become available

again for perhaps another ten years. We had observed the cycles for action that had taken place over the last 50 years.

2. Such an effort must be bipartisan in order to succeed. This was why a crisis was necessary to drive the process.

3. The problem was multifaceted. There were many competing forces that were contributing to the impending crisis, including the elements of supply and demand for health services, both of which were growing at an alarming rate.

4. The issues had to be faced through shared sacrifices by all elements of both the supply and demand sides of health services. In other words, problems of medical services could not be approached through a wish list developed by all participants, which is the historical approach to developing a coalition dedicated to major social change. It was our conclusion that unless the mutual shared sacrifice approach was followed, the process was doomed to failure. What we were saying had been best articulated by President John F. Kennedy when he stated: "Look not to what the country can do for you, but what you can do for your country."

5. In some manner the process of developing the solution and the compromises that were necessary had to be based upon a consensus of experts and not, at least initially, of politicians.

6. The plan as developed should be protected from political appeals based on self interest and should stand upon its merits as a whole.

7. As an approach to the process we proposed that the new president, whoever that might be, should make health reform the first subject for joint action by the Presidency and the Congress to initiate the process, to take a period of approximately two years to be developed and an additional two years to be fully implemented.

8. The President should call upon Congress to authorize and fund a nonpartisan commission of experts nominated by the President and approved by the Congress.

9. The commission should spend approximately a year developing its plan. It could use both public and private meetings to do its work. It should have both paid and volunteer members with a membership large enough to insure representation of viewpoint of the major constituencies. However, the individuals appointed should be selected as individuals and not as designated representatives of constituent groups. Their individual fiduciary obligation should be to the commission and not to any outside group or entity.

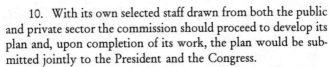

10. With its own selected staff drawn from both the public and private sector the commission should proceed to develop its plan and, upon completion of its work, the plan would be submitted jointly to the President and the Congress.

11. Following the pattern of the current process for closing military bases, after a public hearing or hearings, the Congress could only vote it up or down as a total package. The President would have an overall veto power but if he did so, the proposal would go back to the Congress for a possible override.

By quietly circulating this concept along channels in both parties during the primary process we hoped to avoid the pitfalls that had doomed previous attempts. Our concept obviously did not achieve acceptance nor any serious consideration. The post-election effort by the Clinton Administration followed a political approach which, regardless of the merits of many components of the plan, was doomed to failure as a secretive, partisan effort proposing to create a massive controlled by government system.

In reporting Steve's and my concepts in this volume, my aim is that at some future date this approach may be found to have merit. To provide a discussion base for our proposed process of designing and financing a revised universal healthcare delivery system, Steve and I developed a series of focused issue papers that were based on our experience in dealing with healthcare issues in the real world. Since I believe they are still plausible and of value to future action on healthcare reform, I include them as appendix 1 and 2 of this volume under the titles, "A Charter for Healthcare Restructuring to Maintain and Improve the Healthcare Status of All Americans in a Cost-Effective Manner" and "The Guiding Principles for a Healthcare Reform Strategy" by Stephen W. Gamble.

25

Managed Care

A s I close out this book it seems appropriate to interject a few comments on the subject of managed care – the hottest topic presently being cussed and discussed in the field of healthcare – as it relates to all the critical issues of cost, quality, availability and access to healthcare by the entire population.

Although there is as yet no clearly accepted definition of managed care, I will suggest that managed care may best be defined as a set of principles or a process created by contract which is intended to provide for (1) security of access to healthcare for the consumer-patient at a fixed price to the third party payor for the services – whether an employer or governmental entity; (2) a focus on wellness and prevention; (3) a commitment for "appropriate" treatments, meaning the most cost-effective care; and (4) the transfer of financial risk from insurer to the selected provider or providers to the greatest extent possible through a variety of economic incentives as an alternative to the classical freedom of choice fee-for-service model.

Unfortunately, the problems and abuses of the managed-care approach arise from the implementation and variances in quality of performance as well as the public perception of the process which, of necessity, involves limitations not only on service but on freedom of choice of providers and utilization of service or facilities. Managed care is both a concept and a process that intervenes in the relationship between the individual healthcare provider and the patient, utilizing a variety of controls to assure quality while controlling cost. In its most basic format, as initiated, it can be described as a rationing of care to assure that what is provided is not only medically justified but also appropriate to the needs of the individual patient, usually as defined by contract. Since the term "rationing" is highly inflammatory in the healthcare context, it is rarely used.

The importance of the concept is that at present it is the only viable alternative in the private sector marketplace to a highly regulated single payor system of universal insurance or direct provision of care by a governmental service such as the Canadian system or variations of the various European national plans. The actual implementation of managed care involves a variety of highly controversial issues, both economic and emotional in character, which are subject to potential abuse and misunderstanding, including such fundamental American values as freedom of choice, fairness, individual responsibility and protection against economic exploitation. The basic friction point between the patient and the managed-care plan arises out of the economic incentives causing the managers to provide or deny care to the patient but also hopefully, to assure improved quality of care in a cost-effective manner.

This is all a part of the continued evolution of health insurance in the U.S. as a social mechanism for financing and making available healthcare on a prepaid competitive market basis. The concept of third party payment initiated by Blue Cross for hospi-

Health Policy – The Hard Way

tal care and Blue Shield for physician care, described earlier, was in the form of a loosely controlled managed care. Initially both programs provided service under a plan contract with selected providers for its subscribers with the plan responsible for making direct payment to the provider for the care. Furthermore, payment was made only to those providers participating in the plan, who were in turn subject to certain minimum standards of performance by either peer review or contract.

As commercial insurers entered the market in force in the 1940s, the concept changed to an indemnity approach under which the insurer in effect reimbursed insured patients for their costs as defined in the insuring agreement. The insurer in effect underwrote the costs and assumed the defined risk while the insured patient could assign the financial benefits or indemnity to the healthcare provider while being financially liable for any charges not covered by the contract.

The major weakness in the system was the lack of effective control over increasing costs charged by healthcare providers, the number of service units demanded by patients and the lack of incentives to care providers to control utilization. Since there was freedom of choice of physician the issue of quality of care was not as critical as it would become under managed care. But the economic incentive was for possible overutilization, since the provider was paid on a unit-of-service basis. It was essentially employer based without any mandate upon the part of any employer to provide and/or pay for the insurance premiums. As a result many employers, particularly smaller ones, elected to provide no health insurance. As health coverage costs increased at a rate in excess of the cost of living index, there was enhanced pressure by the business community and individuals to obtain relief. The alternative was terminating the provision of insurance.

During the Nixon administration there was legislation to authorize the establishment of federally approved health maintenance organizations (HMOs). These were essentially plans based upon the models of Ross-Loos and Kaiser Permanente, which had originated in California in the 1930s and were essentially mechanisms under which the health plan beneficiary received broad-based healthcare benefits from a defined panel of physicians and hospitals with strictly limited benefits for care outside the plan. Physicians could be employed either by what was called a staff plan or could be in a physician group such as an independent practice association which contracted with the plan to provide the professional service.

Usually these physicians were affiliated with hospitals either owned by or having contracts with the plan. The plan negotiated with the providers and hospitals for discounts as well as for to control utilization. Although the plan limited the freedom of choice for physicians and hospitals, as well as for specialists, it also introduced a variety of control procedures to limit overutilization, particularly in regards to specialists and inpatient hospital service.

The traditional independent fee-for-service physicians strongly opposed the spread of the HMO movement and initially were effective in limiting its spread. Following the collapse of the Clinton health reform package in 1994, in order to control costs there was strong pressure upon employers and other entities funding healthcare benefits to consider what are now called managed-care plans.

The initial result has been a substantial lowering of the pattern of increased health insurance costs, primarily as the consequence of the reduction in utilization of healthcare services. Savings come by substantially reducing hospital and physician utilization, as well as by negotiated discounts of charges by both physicians and hospitals. A key to the effectiveness of the cost-saving procedures was the strict limitation on the freedom of patient choice of provider while directing patients to preselected physicians and hospitals by contract. This is basic marketplace economics – controlling the costs of units of service and the utilization of services by imposing on providers an array of negative incentives.

Critics of single payer say we won't be able to choose your own doctor - you can't many now, under private plans. They have to be in network

272

Although managed care will not in itself provide a solution for the national problem of the uninsured, it can in part contribute to an evolutionary solution by more effectively utilizing healthcare resources and reducing the cost increases that come with the freedom of choice in the fee-for-service system. But managed care is not without serious problems which must be resolved if it is to provide an alternative to a single payor system of government financed and controlled care. We want to avoid another mandated entitlement, but the managed-care plans have been their own worst enemy, causing the media to demonize the whole movement.

There is no question but that the healthcare system as we have known it was basically inefficient, both operationally and in its priorities. But as managed-care plans have wrung the fat out of the system, to a greater or lesser extent in highly publicized instances they have abused their economic power in order to reward their promoters excessively rather than pass the savings back to the patients and the purchasers of care in both the public and private sector. This has created an anticipation by Wall Street that there can be continued major cost savings to justify their high stock values and compensation. The easy money has been made and now they need to face the fact that future earnings must come from value-added performance with the emphasis on quality. They need to prove that quality is cost effective and patient friendly.

Historically, managed-care savings have come through cuts in payment to providers. In the future managed care must be justified by managing patient care on a case-by-case basis to meet patient needs. The plans have claimed that by using management techniques they can enhance the effectiveness of care on a prevention basis. In other words, their incentive must be to keep patients well. This means they must restructure the care of 25 or 30 percent of the patients who are responsible for 80 to 90 percent of the direct patient care costs. Some plans are already doing this but it must become an industry-wide approach. Each plan will need to be of sufficient size to provide the skills and resources to design and implement effective protocols for these costly patients, particularly those who suffer from debilitating chronic problems.

Above all the administrators must become patient friendly, particularly when handling patient grievances. If they do not resolve this problem they will face continued adverse media attacks that will lead to costly legislative activity not in the best interest of anyone. It is to their own disadvantage if they ignore the truth that the public and the media strongly react to what appears to be arbitrary or capricious denials of care or choice of specialists. Such occurrences when widely publicized can only lead to legislative intervention into the practice of medicine, a major evil in itself.

Accepting the need for a patient grievance procedure is only the first step in an extraordinarily complex process. There are a substantial number of individuals and entities involved in what I describe as the feeding chain of healthcare – starting with the employer's selection of a health plan or a multiple array of health plans from which the employee may choose. Both the quality and financial stability of each plan is important, but even more so is the benefit structure each plan provides as well as the grievance procedure available to the patient. In addition, there must be effective communication to the plan subscriber (patient) about the availability of the grievance procedure and its terms.

How the grievance procedure is administered is also vital – is it managed in-house, which can lead to abuse, or by outside entities such as the American Arbitration Association, which may be more costly and cumbersome? Since the grievance procedure is a process it may start out as an in-house process of direct consultation between the parties and then trigger a more formal and binding arbitration with defined remedies. It should be the duty of the plan or employer to provide an ombudsperson service to the aggrieved employee for assistance and monitoring of the process.

Although I find little support for my viewpoint, I have advo-

Health Policy – The Hard Way

cated that employers in selecting health plans for their employees have a legal liability in selecting and supervising the plan to assure employees they have a fair and effective grievance procedure available. This duty is quite clear when the health plan is a qualified ERISA plan and probably rises to the level of a fiduciary accountability, not just a tort negligence standard.

The federal government in administering Medicare and Medicaid programs is now mandating the availability of an appeals process for benefit denials plus tight time limits for action. State law or regulation applied to insurers of managed-care plans may also mandate grievance procedures, including possible ultimate appeal through a state-established administrative procedure. Some plans have developed professional panels to review individual claims for adjudicating questions such as denial of coverage for treatments deemed experimental or not generally accepted in practice. The medical profession has an ethical obligation to assure that well qualified experts are available to staff such panels, because these panels must be qualified to determine whether or not the procedure requested is medically acceptable as a standard of practice and appropriate for the needs of a particular patient.

When the California Legislature adopted the Friedman-Knowles Act in 1996, (Health and Safety Code 1370.4 and Insurance Code 10145.3), it required that by July 1, 1998, health plans must provide for independent qualified experts' review of denials of coverage for experimental or investigational treatment for patients with terminal conditions. It also mandated the disclosure of the availability of outside review and how to access this. As part of this pattern of increased regulation the Legislature adopted Health and Safety Code 1381.1, Insurance Code 1023.67, stating the plans must file a written policy statement with their regulatory agency describing how they determine whether a second opinion is necessary and how they review requests for second opinions. Although plans are not required to cover second opinions, they must give notice to their subscribers explaining how a person covered by the plan may receive one.

These and other administrative requirements are part of the state's expanded regulatory action relating to managed health plans as the Legislature reacts to reported litigation and media reactions to highly emotional individual cases. What the media fail to report is that these are not new problems nor are they limited to managed-care plans. We have always had problems with the administration of insurance coverage exclusions for experimental or unproven treatment under the fee-for-service and indemnity plans but they did not receive similar publicity.

To aggravate the problem of patients' rights and limitations on insurance coverage is the process of evaluating new and often extraordinarily costly healthcare technology. Although the Food and Drug Administration examines scientific evidence on the safety and efficacy of investigational pharmaceuticals, biotechnological and medical devices, and provides continued surveillance activities over these products to detect adverse events, there is no similar supervision of safety and effectiveness of much of the new technology or treatments.

Reacting to budget pressures, the Congressional Office of Technology Assessment was shut down in 1995 and although a number of federal agencies perform limited service in this area, there is no coördinated effort. The agencies that exercise a degree of responsibility for their respective constituents include the Prospective Payment Commission for updating the payment system for Medicare beneficiaries, the Physician Payment Review Commission, the Department of Veterans Affairs and the General Accounting Office and the Congressional Budget Office.

As a result this critical role is by default being passed to the private sector, including the healthcare provider entities as well as the insurers and managed-care plans. This is a major healthcare policy problem, which must be resolved by joint and coöperative action by all the key players. This should be on the agenda of every patients' rights or health provider organization to avoid the continued conflict in the decision-making process.

In monitoring the quality of the healthcare system, there is now a major shift in the technique of overseeing the process away from what was basically an audit of the procedures of the individual healthcare providers by the Joint Commission on the Accreditation of Hospitals and similar voluntary organizations in various identified classes of providers. Basically these organizations checked the records to determine if approved practices and journals were established and monitored. The shift now is to monitor patient or population healthcare outcomes. This is far more complicated and costly and the standards and procedures for evaluating "outcomes" is in an early evolutionary stage requiring the creation of clear objective consequences to be shared with the purchasers and utilizer of the product.

As health plans move from the frenzy of competitive cost cutting, they must now perform a leadership role in providing the tools and the database for establishing outcome standards and the methodology of monitoring them. They must also make it possible for purchasers of healthcare to have the necessary information for choosing plans while providing a level playing field for competition between providers and plans. Success for managed-care plans will be substantially based on their ability to integrate the entire patient care process, including all classes of providers. In addition, the managed-care plans should have the ability to develop sophisticated communication plus a database that will make it possible to relate treatment protocols to outcomes while adjusting for other controlling factors such as age, sex, preëxisting condition and relevant factors, including cost and availability of service.

Beyond this, managed-care plans must be seen as credible to patients and employers in order to verify that the patient has received value for what was paid for the care and the risk assumed.

This will lead to the potential of multiple layers of coverage with appropriate premium structures and also make possible greater freedom of choice by the patient and a possible sharing of the risk. One would hope such steps would lead to better overall patient care and convenient access to care.

The managed-care industry is troubled by the fact that a wide disparity in quality of performance leads to increased demand for governmental regulation to assure the financial and management qualifications of each individual plan besides monitoring the denied benefit structure and performance of both the plans and the healthcare providers. Failure to resolve these issues on a voluntary basis will of necessity result in continued expansion of a costly governmental regulatory process based on formalized statements or requirements of patient rights.

The overriding issue is whether the governmental intervention will be on a national basis as an expansion or modification of the federal ERISA statute as it applies to healthcare or will be left to the states. Any attempt to modify ERISA unfortunately runs afoul of overwhelming opposition by major employers and other interests who fight to protect it because of its application to other forms of social insurance, including pension and retirement plans. However, the alternative is a wide smörgåsbord of state action, which is already evolving. Although I am reluctant to encourage federal action, I must admit I favor the adoption of basic preëmptive federal legislation to create minimum standards of benefits, performance and accountability. Although this will be more costly, I believe it is worth the price and it would, hopefully, minimize the necessity of litigation to resolve these issues.

For the long run it is becoming increasingly apparent that the rapid expansion in size and sophistication of fully integrated healthcare delivery systems will lead to an inevitable move to direct contracting between the purchasers of healthcare, whether private employers or governmental entities, and the fully integrated delivery systems–thus bypassing the existing managed-care plans. This will in part eliminate one layer of costs in the total system, but will also raise critical questions as to the ability of healthcare providers to provide the assurance of quality and utilization controls, as well as the role of government as the monitor in default of monitoring by the purchasers of healthcare as they organize themselves into larger and more effective entities.

In my years of experience with healthcare policy problems, never has there been such an opportunity to deal effectively with the structure of healthcare and the basic product as we move from an emphasis on costly inpatient hospital care to alternative care through a variety of outpatient services. I believe that the evolving developments in the field of medicine, both in diagnostic and in treatment procedures, will lead to more effective prevention, better quality and lowered overall cost of care if properly managed for the benefit of patients.

We cannot overlook the truth that this improvement in quality of care will contribute to and increase in the number of elderly patients in our society, who will no longer be making a major contribution to the cost of their care. The challenge is to restructure the system in an effective manner to absorb the costs of both the demand and supply of healthcare. This will require leadership and statespersonship in a sort of system not yet identified, but I believe such a system will ultimately be developed to provide the solutions and compromises. Yet even with these changes there will continue to be tremendous problems for all levels of government in providing a safety net for the uninsured or underinsured population. Here again the managed-care system can make a major contribution to the solution by participating in a partner relationship between the public and private sector in problem solving.

The initial thrust of the managed-care plans was to cut hospital utilization as well as unit costs for each procedure by a variety of approaches, including negotiating a pattern of discounts to hospital charges as a condition of the plan's referral of patients to them. New methods of payment were utilized like paying hospitals a negotiated fixed amount per diem and a maximum per case cost or, in the alternative, paying a negotiated capitated rate for each defined procedure, thus transferring the utilization risk to the hospital or medical group. Particularly for the physician-cost component the managed-care plan might establish a risk pool to cover the physician and/or hospital costs as incurred and provide either a bonus or penalty to be shared by the providers based on the actual performance of the pool.

Cumulatively these approaches were successful and as the managed-care plans' profits skyrocketed they became the darlings of Wall Street. But after media exposure of the extraordinary compensation paid some plan executives who initiated these procedures, coupled with a major shift of many managed-care plans from a not-for-profit status to a profit status, public opinion became increasingly critical. What Wall Street did not fully appreciate was that these were essentially one-time savings and any future savings would be substantially less while the pattern of substantial increased healthcare costs could continue. Also, the healthcare plans themselves added an additional layer of costs of up to 20 or 30 percent of premium; the charge also became the subject of continued criticism.

Healthcare providers moved to create their own structures for their own protection and to participate in the profit potential that seemed available. Initially these included provider-owned or -controlled HMOs, integrated provider groups or independent practice associations of sufficient size and ability to contract directly with the employer groups, eliminating the intermediary share of the health-care dollar taken by the managed-care plans.

A fundamental issue for managed care is the public perception that these plans abuse the authority over access to medical service and freedom of choice of healthcare providers to the detriment of

Health Policy – The Hard Way

patients. This adverse viewpoint is fueled by the media when horror stories are reported and remembered anecdotally by the public. Although many of these are justified, others are misleading because a reporter fails to understand technical details and thus fails to report a balanced story. Thus issues of managed-care abuses have become politicized in a highly emotional atmosphere.

The earliest occurrences involved denials of payment for bone marrow transplants during the time when this extraordinarily expensive procedure was evolving from a high risk experimental strategy to what is now a highly refined successful answer to otherwise fatal conditions. Yet even today this application is not indicated in every case and there are serious problems in selecting the physicians and institutions that can effectively perform it. As with most transplants, there are issues of availability and quality of the donor for the particular recipient.

A critical social and economic issue becomes whether or not a particular plan purchased by or for the patient excludes a specific procedure. Although initially this is a matter of contract, it soon may become a target of regulation or legislative action, as has been the case of the so-called drive-through birthing incidents. Good medicine, social policy and cost of healthcare come into conflict. Not all healthcare is a priority but drawing the line is a necessarily complex emotional issue. One managed-care executive was quoted as saying, "We don't deny care, we just don't pay for it." Although this puts it in a blunt fashion, payment is the issue. What is the patient entitled to and who provides it? The process by which this clash of interests is resolved is a critical one for all healthcare providers and payors.

My experience in dealing with all types of healthcare decisions is that the process by which a decision is made is often as important as the decision itself. This is particularly true with managed healthcare, where the need for open communication and understanding is an overriding obligation of all the participants. The charge that nobody will talk to me or nobody will answer my questions is fatal to the acceptance of those decisions that affect quality of living or life itself.

Appendix 1

Charter for Healthcare Restructuring to Maintain and Improve the Healthcare Status of All Americans in a Cost-Effective Manner

The solution of the complex problem of the cost and access to healthcare for all Americans is universally recognized as a top priority for the nation. However, there is no consensus by the country's leadership as to how this problem can be resolved. The confusing multiplication of conflicting proposals is leading to a polarization of positions which contributes to the acceleration of the increase in the number of Americans who are without insurance or other protection or who are threatened with this potential problem due to unemployment or inability of employers or governmental entities to provide such protection adequately. Continued failure to find a solution will seriously impact the health status of all Americans.

The problem is rapidly becoming critical and is now accepted as a major priority by all political sectors see an approaching crisis that would become intolerable. For the first time since the close of World War II major segments of the population that formerly felt confident of having readily available high-quality healthcare now feel insecure and potentially threatened.

For the purposes of this statement it is not necessary to further document the existence and threat of the problem. Unfortunately, there is no consensus as to a realistic and achievable solution to the complex problem. There is no lack of short-term and long-term proposals. However, none of these to date, no matter how well intended, are able to attract any politically achievable consensus. All fail to deal effectively with the complex factors that have contributed to the strengths and weaknesses of the current system with its intertwining relationship between the public and private shared responsibility and the finite resources that can be dedicated to an acceptable solution. The fact that the burden is felt by all levels of government – federal, state and local entities – coupled with a major burden borne by many but not all employers, as well as individu-

Appendix 1   283

als, leads to increasing avoidance or shifting of the burden that is in competition with other critical social needs.

There is increasing recognition that all the participants involved in the availability of healthcare, whether as providers, funders or consumers of care, must contribute to the solution through a variety of ways. This recognition has increasingly polarized the ability or willingness of any component to make a unilateral contribution or sacrifice to the solution of the problem or face realistically the potential damage of a failure to act.

Of equal importance is the fact that proposed solutions are becoming increasingly the subject of polarized partisan politics of a far more complex nature than just major party rivalry. As a result, the potential for a negotiated or even a compromise solution becomes ever more remote. Additionally, many of the most popular solutions would simply increase funding or subsidization without fundamental restriction necessary to achieve cost effectiveness. The popular solutions will be counter-productive and aggravate the cost spiral.

Any effective approach to restructuring the system requires coördinated action at all government levels as well as by the private sector, involving complexities beyond the ability of the political process to handle. Consequently, inaction or a series of frustrating partial solutions designed to paper over the problem will continue to be pursued. A comprehensive solution will be deferred until we have a true catastrophe: a major collapse of the availability of health services to a major segment of the population – particularly the so-called "middle class" who heretofore have been substantially protected by the existence of employer-provided health insurance. It is likely the triggering mechanism will be the collapse of our overtaxed, underfunded emergency care centers coupled with the increased withdrawal of employer-provided insurance.

Under these evolving circumstances what approach would appear to have the greatest potential? It appears that what is needed is a rational process leading to the development and implementation of potential solutions – not an imposed mandate from on high. The circumstances for designing and implementing an effective process are fortuitous for a variety of reasons.

1. There is now a public realization of the cost and inadequacies of the present system. Although this is not combined with an understanding of the complexity of the factors involved, there is a fear of the future and a demand for some sort of action, however rational or irrational.

2. This is a national election year which will lead to the selection of a president for the next four years. Such a time is propitious for furnishing an opportunity for the elected candidate, of whichever party, to have the ability to undertake a creative solution to a major problem, one that is not necessarily universally acceptable or politically palatable, but which must be

Health Policy – The Hard Way

undertaken in the public interest or potentially deferred for another four years. In this regard the current political campaign will only highlight the issues without solving them.

3. For the first time in many years there will be a substantial change in the constituency of both the House and the Senate which will not only require a rethinking of obsolete positions but will stimulate the need and urgency for effective action and a greater willingness to explore new approaches, particularly anything that has the potential of mobilizing a consensus on the health issues. Then Congress can concentrate on other issues critical to their constituencies.

4. For the first time since the adoption of Titles XVIII and XIX in 1965 there is a demand by business, labor and the general public that there must be some action on this high priority problem which is closely linked with the problems of a recession, heavy unemployment and the prospect of a slow recovery. Never in the last seventeen years has the demand for action (however ill-defined) been so great and building in momentum.

❦ *Proposal for Bipartisan Action*

The candidate elected as President for the next four years will be encouraged to make the resolution of the availability, access and cost of quality healthcare a major part of his state-of-the-union address and a priority for his four year administration.

He will explain the complexities of the issue and the need for an innovative and, above all else, a bipartisan approach to the problem. The proposal will be to create a 15-member commission with a title such as "The Bipartisan Commission" to develop an action plan for the restructuring of the healthcare system.

The commission will be given a specific mission and deadlines. Its mission will be to develop an action plan designed to utilize effectively the resources dedicated to the provision of healthcare for all Americans on a realistic and cost-effective basis. To assure fairness to the recipients and the providers of healthcare the development of the plan will take the first year of the commission activity, with not to exceed three years to effectively phase in the various components of change that will be required at the federal, state, local and private sector levels.

Although the commission itself will have no authority to mandate action by any of the affected sectors except by acceptance of its program validity, it will have the responsibility to monitoring performance and report annually on the progress and shortfalls of implementation. The commission will also have the authority to modify its recommendations based on actual developments.

The commission will develop its own agenda for action but will be required to follow certain basic principles such as:

1. All sectors responsible for providing healthcare must avoid or be

a miracle that act happened so fast

denied the right to cost shift to other sectors.

2. The maintenance and enhancement of quality of care must be a prime objective.

3. Unnecessary duplication of high cost facilities and programs shall be discouraged.

4. The realignment of the incentives for cost and quality for various classes of healthcare will be a prime objective.

5. The availability and licensure of all classes of healthcare professionals will be reviewed to encourage the effective use of highly trained healthcare personnel.

6. Emphasis on personal responsibility for effective use of healthcare resources and costs, including emphasis on primary care and prevention.

7. Need for innovative approaches emphasizing American values with continued research and use of demonstration projects at all levels.

The commission will thoroughly review its role and define the responsibility for determining that the provision of unnecessary or redundant care be minimized, and that care be provided at the most efficient and effective level as to cost and performance outcomes. A system of accountability will be maintained to continuously eliminate the provision of outdated or contraindicated services and procedures.

A major thrust of the commission will be to eliminate at all levels costly overhead that does not contribute to efficient care.

Structure

The commission will be created by Congressional action and provided with the necessary authority and financial resources to perform its mission.

The commission will be appointed by the President with the approval of the Senate, provided that a high level bipartisan advisory group will be created to help select as commissioners highly qualified individuals who have the status to receive the respect that will lead to effective acceptance and implementation of their action plan.

The membership shall be limited to 15, who shall receive a four-year appointment.

Although a full-time commitment will not be required, especially during the first year, a substantial time commitment will be expected and appropriate. Modest remuneration will be provided in addition to reimbursement for all appropriate expenses.

Individual appointees will not be required to leave existing employment or positions provided that adequate protection against conflict of interest will be arranged.

The constituency of the commission will emphasize problem solving and creative leadership rather than representing vested interests.

It is anticipated that to meet the time deadlines the commission will break down into task forces to consider particular problem areas, such as the effective utilization of high technology, the integration of the health-care components of workers' compensation, auto accidents, long-term care and personal licensure. The commission as a whole will be responsible for acting on all task force reports and integrating the results into a unified whole.

The commission will be encouraged to make interim recommendations for defined courses of action to avoid delays. Similarly, federal, state and private agencies will be encouraged to develop and implement experimental or demonstration projects to test new ideas and concepts, such as effective use of practice protocols, outcome measurements, and the like.

> The commission will be encouraged to recognize the differences in need and utilization of healthcare and to build on the strengths and variations in the existing systems, both rural and urban as well as geographical and cultural.
>
> The commission shall be concerned about the impact of change or the failure to change upon the competitive economic status of not only the nation but also as between states.
>
> The commission will place increased emphasis upon the responsibility of individuals for the results of their life-style choices.

Not as a mandate to the commission but as an aid to its development of agenda, as well as information to those who must consider the complexity of the issues involved and the degree of involvement and commitment required by all sectors of the nation if the process is to be successful, a series of schedules are attached which are illustrative but not definitive. In part this listing is to encourage all interested parties to reëvaluate the items by adding, deleting and suggesting priorities of action toward a movement to a consensus. Above all else, this approach will emphasize that all components of society must make major contributions to the ultimate solution as it is phased into place and provides a firm basis for continued future action.

> Schedule One sets forth a preliminary set of goals and objectives for the restructuring process against which all proposals can be judged.
>
> Schedule Two is an initial list of the possible contributions or sacrifices that may be required of all the major sectors involved in the provision, funding or consumption of healthcare.
>
> Schedule Three is an initial list of the barriers to change which must be overcome. This list clearly identifies the need for specific time frames for action.
>
> Schedule Four is an initial list of non-exclusive potential action areas.

Appendix 2

The Guiding Principles for a Healthcare Reform Strategy

by Stephen W. Gamble

American society thrives on instant gratification. Whether it is an individual's way of life, a corporate business practice, or the political process, results are anticipated to be immediate. Problems are addressed by a quick-fix, or they are not addressed.

Such is the case of healthcare reform in the last decade of this century. Fixes, large and small, abound with the large ones being too costly and/or controversial to be adopted and the small ones only dealing peripherally with the problem. In this quandary for our society, as the situation worsens something will be done about it, but it won't necessarily be the best thing to do unless key participants have thought through and effectively defined the issues.

The healthcare "crisis" of the 1990s is a problem not of the rich versus the poor; it is a case of the insured versus the un- or underinsured. It is a matter of convincing the 70 percent of the population who have the healthcare gratification they want to give that up in favor of "something else" that will include the 30 percent have-nots. This is a critical obstacle to success for any quick fix reform proposal.

Faced with this reality the rational thing to do is to take a series of incremental reform steps based upon long-range principles around which the healthcare system of tomorrow should be shaped. When the key participants have concurred in the *principles* of an effective healthcare system for the U.S. society, then all the components of our current system and proposals for reform can be evaluated and modified according to these criteria:

a) Do they help society move toward its objective for healthcare, or
b) Do they hinder the ability of society to move toward its objective for healthcare?

Following is an outline of potential principles and process for achieving a long-range healthcare reform strategy.

The Guiding Principles for a healthcare reform strategy must be broad enough to encompass the wide range of expectations of the major players in their implementation: government, business, labor, providers, payors and consumers. They must also be realistically achievable while not being so specific as to divide the major players before the evaluation process has even begun.

The following prototype principles are drawn from a considerable volume of prior work. The goal of the principles is to outline the elements around which it can be agreed the healthcare system should be molded and developed.

Principal 1 – Health Status: The fundamental objective of the healthcare system is to achieve the best possible health status of the population at a cost society is willing and able to afford.

This objective is too often taken for granted in most reform proposals. It cannot go without saying. No amount of reform will achieve utopia. There will be limits, and there will be trade-offs; the parties, and particularly the public, should be given the opportunity to understand what the expectation for benefit and cost of each reform will be, as measured against a basic standard. All will have to make concessions along the way, including government, providers, employers, individuals and third-party payors.

Reaching agreement among the parties as to an appropriate cost/benefit standard will be exceedingly difficult. However, many reform initiatives can proceed while this important part of the equation is being worked out. No doubt each new reform proposal will impart to the parties a new sense of urgency for agreement on a basic cost/benefit standard.

It is conceivable for society to decide that in order to achieve its health status *and* other objectives, the cost of healthcare should not exceed X percent of the GNP by the end of the decade. Such a determination, if reached through a deliberative process that considers what is and is not to be counted as healthcare cost and how it is to be measured, could be extremely helpful in setting healthcare priorities and in restructuring the system around these.

Principle 2 – Accessibility: All individuals must have access to at least basic healthcare services, but not all healthcare is a priority. Access to medically necessary healthcare is now generally accepted as a basic human right and an essential condition for productive participation in society. However, society has not yet placed an evaluation on the healthcare wish list in order to distinguish between need and demand. The difficulty arises in defining an appropriate set of basic healthcare services that will fit most circumstances and at a cost society is willing and able to afford.

Principle 3 – Affordability: Healthcare must be delivered effectively and efficiently at a cost which individuals, organizations and society can afford without risking serious medical or financial consequences.

All the parties agree on this principle, but none seem to agree on how to accomplish it. Here the evaluation process is of major importance. Each element must be reduced to its lowest common denominator and challenged as to:

a) What is it we do (or propose to do) that hinders our ability to achieve this objective?
b) What is it we do (or propose to do) that helps our ability to achieve this objective?

Marketplace competition, for example, both hinders and helps society to achieve this objective. The healthcare marketplace, because of the overriding impact of healthcare and the role of the physician in designating both the quantity and source of the care, is not subject to marketplace competition in the classic sense. Any reform proposal must be evaluated in terms of how it will improve those marketplace factors that exist and which help affordability and remove those factors which hinder it. To the extent that marketplace values are not effective, alternative controls and incentives in the public interest must be adopted.

Principle 4 – Basic Healthcare Services: Basic healthcare services, to the extent society is willing to provide the resources, must cover a range of care from preventive through long-term, designed to avoid illness, restore health and alleviate suffering. The basic healthcare services should be managed under effective standards of medical necessity and appropriateness. What is desirable and what is doable under this principle are two vastly different things. A process for implementing the doable, one step at a time on a priority basis, is required, and that process would be enhanced if there was in place the basic cost/benefit standard outlined under principle 1.

Assuming that such a standard will not be available in the near term, the evaluative process should work backwards from a list of services that are desirable in the future to a list of services that are doable now, taking into consideration other factors which would affect the affordability of selected services. Such "other factors" would include managed care and "rigorous" standards of medical necessity and appropriateness.

Principle 5 – Quality: An established standard of quality is an integral part of access to affordable healthcare services. That standard should

Health Policy – The Hard Way

encompass an individual's single encounter with a healthcare provider, the total range of care the individual receives and the overall care provided to the risk groups the individual represents. Furthermore that standard should consider the resources necessary to provide the quality of healthcare being recommended.

As society's ability to effectively evaluate the quality of healthcare improves, it becomes feasible to establish norms of behavior and outcome above which performance is encouraged and below which performance is unacceptable. The application of such standards help protect individuals receiving care as well as validate to society its judgment of the value it is receiving from the system. However, the cost of providing and evaluating the quality standards of practice must not be isolated from the process of establishing access and affordability under future reform proposals.

Principle 6 – Adequately and Fairly Financed: The healthcare system should be financed through a pluralistic, public/private sector division of responsibilities which will adequately and fairly cover the costs of providing the committed level of benefit for each respective beneficiary group.

This principle relies upon the major parties coming together in agreement that, no matter what one or another of the parties might prefer as a first choice, the reality is there will not be a major shift to public financing of healthcare in America in this decade because such a move would be extremely complex, involve considerable voter risk, because the tax base necessary to support it is not now available. On the other hand, the role of government as a regulator of the cost and quality of healthcare will increase in effectiveness as quantifiable standards and measurable outcomes become more reliable and publicly acceptable. The emphasis of reform must be placed on a more effective use of existing healthcare resources. When the size, and shape and results of the healthcare product can be measured, there can be no reason for paying the provider less than what it costs to deliver that product, and to prosper, as with any other essential enterprise in America.

Principle 7 – Efficiently Delivered: The management of healthcare costs is a shared responsibility. Delivery and financing mechanisms should align the incentives of the patient, the payor and the provider to promote continuous improvement in the efficient use of resources and, wherever feasible, eliminate conflicts of interest, redundant administration, unnecessary duplication and the furnishing of services inappropriate to the individual need.

Providers must be accountable to patients, payors and, ultimately, the public for the efficient delivery of healthcare. However, as long as many of the incentives for patients, payors and providers favor over-utilization rather than effective utilization, costs will be unnecessarily elevated. Experience has shown that regulation on its own will not materially change behavior without a collateral positive incentive for the involved individuals and organizations to do differently in their own interest. In fact, regulation often legitimizes a way of doing business that may not be the most appropriate.

On the consumption side the American propensity for instant gratifications carries over into an almost insatiable demand for healthcare products and services by those who have the means to pay for them (health insurance) and access to the system. On the supply side the *cost* of healthcare in America includes not just the cost of a given product or service but also the number of units of a product or services delivered, administration of the paying process, quality and utilization controls, complicated interrelationships between patients, physicians, hospitals and third-party payors, licensure, ethical considerations, laws and regulations. While all of these provide a benefit to society, each has its own baggage of costly disadvantages that must be addressed.

The logical approach to cost control of healthcare in America is neither to foster more competition of the present kind nor to regulate, but to organize a system of care that is self-regulating through appropriate incentives and priorities.

Principle 8 – Technologically Sound: Technological advances in healthcare should be centrally evaluated in terms of measurable outcome versus cost with the results published so that individuals and organizations can make relatively informed decisions whether to use, pay for or provide a specific technology.

America is the last bastion in the world where sufficient incentive remains to spur a considerable and often risky investment in new healthcare technology development. This circumstance also spurs the expenditure of scarce healthcare resources on unnecessary or questionable procedures and technology. However, if in the interest of cost containment, America's incentives are blunted to the point where investment in research and development is significantly curtailed, present and future generations will be denied access to a whole host of legitimate and worthwhile healthcare improvements.

Rather than stop the flow of new developments, the process should help the buyer be aware of what works and what doesn't so that in large measure only those developments that have proven themselves to work will reap the benefit of the enterprise incentive.

Appendix 3

Barriers and Structural Problems in Effecting Healthcare System Reform

In critiquing any proposed healthcare reform or restructuring, whether at the state or national level, it is useful to have a delineated set of problems or barriers that must be resolved or overcome against which each proposal can be judged as to feasibility of implementation and potential effectiveness. The anticipated results will differ depending upon whether the proposal is limited to an individual state or is of national scope. Depending on the particular design of a reform proposal many of these matters may or may not be relevant. By delineating these barriers and system problems it is also possible to identify those forces or vested interests that will oppose the proposed changes or which will be positively or negatively affected.

1. For Hospitals
   a. Legal and structural inability to reduce the cost burden of excess capacity caused by:
      – Inflexibility of institutional licensure that prevents the effective use of redundant capacity for other types of care, such as skilled nursing, rehabilitation, psychiatric, long term care, outpatient and the like.
      – Reimbursement policies that create adverse incentives to conversions. Although designed to prevent abuse, the result may be counter-productive in the effective use of resources.
      – Antitrust limitations on coöperative actions to use the facilities of competing institutions more effectively or to eliminate surplus community capacity.
      – Competition for managed-care contracts that create an incentive for hospitals to provide a complete spectrum of healthcare services rather than concentrate on the services most needed by the community and sharing services and facilities based on need.
      –Existence of surplus of specialists and super-specialists who de-

mand the availability of the state-of-the-art high-tech facilities and personnel in every facility.

– Barriers to creation of effective vertical integration of the provision of healthcare to include prevention, inpatient and outpatient care, including home care and hospice services.

b. Failure to provide effective limits on the further creation of redundant healthcare facilities where there is no demonstrated need and encouragement of the continued proliferation of:

– Freestanding surgery facilities, recovery facilities or imaging centers.

– Unneeded expansion of existing institutions.

c. Continuation of healthcare payment policies that fail to align the economic incentives of physicians and hospitals, such as:

– Payment for hospitals on a case or per diem basis.

– Payment of physicians on a unit of service basis.

– Prohibition against hospital employment of physicians.

– Antitrust or legal barriers to combination of doctors and hospitals in cost saving and quality improvement arrangements.

– Difficulties in combining hospital, physician and plan liability coverage with incentives for cost savings and injury prevention.

2. Physicians
   a. Availability

   – The existing and continued distortion based on the ratio of specialists to primary care physicians and the possible underpayment of primary care physicians as contrasted with possible overpayment of specialists.

   – The method of funding medical education that encourages medical schools to overemphasize the training of specialists.

   – The debt burden on medical school graduates that distorts their choice of location for service.

   – The university and medical school competition for prestige programs.

   – Lack of adequate incentives to engage in rural or deprived area practice.

   b. Barriers by antitrust to effective limitation on substandard or redundant practice patterns by the development and enforcement of practice protocols.

   c. Arbitrary limitations on the right to combine to negotiate fees.

   d. Are statutory prohibition on balance billing, other limitations on billing such as unbundling, payment for services outside of protocols, etc., or use of outcome measurements appropriate?

3. Antitrust
   There is a basic problem of conflicts between DOJ and FTC on the

one hand and HHS on the other regarding the role and effect of competition on the cost and availability of healthcare. The conflicting policies are confusing, costly and counter-productive and clearly indicate a need for a coördinated national policy.

4. Human Resources
   a. Increased pattern of a proliferation of personal licensure categories limiting the ability to efficiently utilize high cost personnel in a time of rapid changes in technology and practice patterns.
   b. Lack of personnel with new skills in patient care management and in gate-keeper roles.
   c. Decrease in number of nursing schools.
   d. The need for a career ladder in nursing as well as continued flexibility in utilization.
   e. Possible use of institutional licensure as a substitute for personal licensure.

5. Insurance Barriers
   a. ERISA is an arbitrary barrier to effective reform action at the state level. There is a need for greater flexibility to permit states to develop creative reform plans that will solve each state's special needs or practice patterns.
   b. Role of State Insurance Commission and National Association of Insurance Commissioners.
   c. Creation of independent agency to supervise the system.
   d. Legislated or administrative created controls for:
      –Mandated benefits, coverage, transferability and guaranteed renewal.
      – Rate bands.
      – Extended coverage on termination.
      – Periodic open enrollment.
      – Participation in pools for uninsurable individuals or groups.
      – Cherry picking of market.
      – Part-time worker coverage.
      – Coverage for small employers or individuals.
      – Establishing basic benefit package.
      – Catastrophic and long-term coverage.
      – Mandated qualification of plan medical director or other persons making plan decisions on coverage.
      – Coverage for emergency care by out-of-plan providers.
   e. Barriers created by state laws to managed-care plans.
      – Mandated benefits or coverage such as acupuncture, drug addiction, etc.
      – Mandated freedom of choice and continuation of benefits or selected healthcare provider.

 – Requirement that all qualified physicians be permitted to partic-
ipate (any willing provider).
 – Limitation on underwriting requirements for specified groups.
 – Mandated coverage for specified groups.
 – Mandated participation in pools.
 – Limits on premiums.
 – Mandated due process for selection or deselection of contract
providers by health plans or integrated medical group.

6. Patient Grievance Mechanism for the Entire Spectrum
 a. Mandated or voluntary, including by contract.
 b. How administered–internally or by outside entity.
 c. Parties covered on both the provider and consumer side.
 d. Time limits for steps in process.
 e. Final and binding action or advisory.
 f. How initiated and existence of special rules and conflict of interest
issues.
 g. Scope of authority to act.
 h. Possible final appeal to state agency.
 i. Availability of ombudsperson.
 j. Method of selection and qualification of arbitrators.
 k. How financed.
 l. Confidentiality.
 m. Substitution for tort action.

Publications and Papers

by the Author (Chronologically)

"Evaluating Liability Insurance," *Hospitals,* Vol. 29, February 1955.

"Problems in the Control of Hospital Costs," paper, Conference on Health and Welfare, Los Angeles, February 5, 1955.

"Public and Professional Liability," *Hospital Progress,* November 1955.

"Guide to a Planned Safety Program," *Hospitals,* Vol. 29, Dec. 1955.

"Consents: A Realistic Approach," *Hospital Progress,* January 1956.

"Workshops Stress Higher Standards of Practice for Accident Prevention," *Hospitals,* Vol. 31, February 16, 1957.

"Disclosure of Medical Record Information: A Reappraisal," *Hospitals,* Vol. 31, July 16, 1957.

"Subpoenas for Hospital Records," *Los Angeles Bar Bulletin,* Sept. 1957.

"Bedrails: Up or Down?" *Hospitals,* Vol. 31, November 16, 1957.

"What Hospitals Should Know About Investigational Drugs," *Hospitals,* Jan. 1958.

"Outlining the Trustee's Legal Responsibilities," *Trustee,* Vol. 11, August 1958.

"Group Malpractice Insurance Programs," *The Bulletin of the Los Angeles County Medical Association,* October 16, 1958.

"Admitting the Patient: A Matter of Good Form," *Hospitals,* May 26, 1959.

"Hospital – Physician Liability: How State Medicolegal Committees Can Make Patient Care Better and Safer," *Hospitals,* Vol. 33, July 16, 1959.

"Elements of Nonprofit Trusteeship," presented at the 1960 Annual Conference of Blue Cross Plans, April 3, 1960.

"Social Welfare Versus Efficiency," *Hospital Forum,* August 1960.

"Better Patient Care through Group Professional Liability Insurance," *Hospitals,* March 16, 1961.

"Validity of the Formulary System in California," *Hospital Forum,* July 1961.

"Problems of Patient Identification in Hospitals," *Hospital Forum,* September 1961.

"Medical Staff Organization and Membership," *Hospital Forum,* October 1961.

"The Hospital Attorney – Fish or Fowl?" *Hospitals,* Vol. 36, Dec. 1, 1962; *Trustee,* Vol. 16, Jan. 1963.

"Nonprofit Hospitals and Unemployment Insurance," *Hospitals,* Feb. 16, 1963.

"The Significance of a Sound Guiding Principles for Hospitals Program," *Hospital Forum,* April 1963.

"Guidelines For an Effective Emergency Department," *Hospitals,* June 16, 1963.

"Medical Staff Privileges: Legal Snares for the Hospital," *Hospitals,* Vol. 38, Aug. 1, 1964; *Trustee,* Vol. 17, September 1964.

"A Model Agreement For Full-Time Physician Coverage of Emergency Service," *Hospitals,* Vol. 41, March 1, 1967; *Trustee,* Vol. 20:3, March 1967.

"Super Incentives: Swift Route to Hospital Efficiency," *Hospitals,* Dec. 1967.

"Contracts For Hospital Administrators," American College of Hospital Administrators, *Administrative Briefs,* Vol. II, No. 2, July 1968.

"Contracts for Hospital Administrators–An Attorney's View," *Trustee,* Nov. 1968.

"California Nonprofit Corporations, Chapter 7, Tort and Contract Liability," *California Bar Association Practice Manual,* 1969.

"Background to Comprehensive Health Planning," paper, Orientation Conf. on Comprehensive Health Planning, L.A., March 22, 1969.

"Report on California" *Report of Senate Subcommittee on Executive Reorganization, Medical Malpractice: The Patient Versus the Physician,* Nov. 20, 1969

"Physician–Hospital Relations: The Role of Staff Privileges," *Law and Contemporary Problems,* Vol. 35, No. 4, Autumn "1970, Duke Univ. School of Law.

"Arbitration," (with Howard Hassard), *Hospitals,* Vol. 44, Oct. 1, 1970.

"Why Patients Sue," book review on *Exploring the Medical Malpractice Dilemma* by Cyril H. Wecht, *Hospitals,* Vol. 47, Feb. 1, 1973.

"Legal Rights and Responsibilities of Governing Boards and Hospital Staffs," paper, 1973 National Medicolegal Symposium, ABA/AMA.

"Legal Liability and Medical Care Audit," Monograph Medical Care Audit, 1974.

"The Legal Aspect of Obtaining Medical Staff Privileges In a New Community," *The Journal of Legal Medicine,* Sept./Oct.1974.

"Strengthening the Legal Position of Catholic Health Facilities," *Hospital Progress,* October 1974.

"Health Maintenance Organizations HMOs: Do They Really Work?" *The Forum,* Vol. X, No. 1, Fall 1974.

"Malpractice: Funding Emerges As a Critical Issue," *Hospitals,* March 16, 1976; *Hospital Medical Staff,* Vol. 5, No. 3, March 1976; *Trustee,* April 1976.

"Medicolegal Review–Physician Rehabilitation: A Better Alternative to Punishment," *Hospital Medical Staff,* Vol. 5, No. 4, April 1976.

"Malpractice: Simple Solution Eludes Tort Reformists," *Trustee,* Vol. 29, No. 6, June 1976.

"Reports in Two States Suggest Solutions to Malpractice Crisis," *Hospitals,* Vol. 51, No. 6, March 16, 1977.

"States Move Toward Legislated Hospital Risk Management," *Hospitals,* Vol. 51, No. 10, May 16, 1977.

"Helping the Impaired Physician," *Trustee,* Vol. 31, No. 10, Oct. 1978.

"Informed Consents," pamphlet, Am. Hospital Association, Nov. 1978.

Review of "Informed Consent," in *American Journal of Law & Medicine,* Vol. 5, No. 2, 1979.

"The Hospital Dilemma–the Voluntary Effort," *Pacemaker,* Jan. 1979.

"Hiring a CEO Made (Almost) Easy," *Trustee,* June 1979.

"Risk Management for Hospitals and Healthcare Institutions," and "Risk Management on a State Program Basis: The California Experience and Arbitration." *Practicing Law Institute,* 1979.

"Good Samaritan Laws: Do State Statutes Protect your EMS Staff?" *Hospital Medical Staff,* Vol. 9, No. 11, Nov. 1980.

"Formal Instrument Counts: Yes or No?" (with James N. Wright) *Hospital Medical*

Staff, Vol. 11, No. 3, March 1982.

"Hospital – Physician Relationships: Case Studies and Commentaries on Medical Staff Problems," *Journal of Legal Medicine,* Vol. 4, 1983.

"Payment Systems, Cost Management, and Malpractice," *Hospitals,* Nov. 1984.

"Legal Counsel For the Medical Staff," *Hospital Law Newsletter,* December 1984.

"Channeling and Other Strategies For Managing the Next Malpractice Crisis For Hospitals and Physicians" and "An Analysis of the Causes and Problems Leading to the Coming Crisis in the Cost and Availability of Malpractice Insurance," papers, American Academy of Hospital Attorneys, June 5, 1985.

"California's Landmark Medical Injury Compensation Reform Act: Upheld Again but Subject to Continuing Challenge," *Legal Counsel,* September 1985.

"1985-1995: A Decade of Dynamic Evolution in Hospital/Physician Relations – – The Hospital Perspective," paper at American Academy of Hospital Attorneys Symposium, November 18-19, 1985.

"Evaluation of the California Experience With the Medical Injury Compensation Reform Act of 1975 (MICRA)," Report to Senator Hatch, U.S. Senate, 1986.

"California Medical Malpractice Tort Reform," *Legal Counsel,* Fall 1987.

"California Medical Malpractice Tort Reform: An Update – Part II," *Legal Counsel,* Summer 1988.

"Neonatal Brain Injury: The Foremost Medical Liability Problem," Calif. Invitational II, *CAHHS Insight,* Vol. 13, No. 4, May 30, 1989.

"The Battle For Medical Malpractice Tort Reform, A Report From the Front Lines," paper at annual meeting, American Academy of Hospital Attorneys, June 25-28, 1989.

"Medical Malpractice and Tort Reform: A Summary and Look to the Future," *Medical Staff Counselor,* Vol. 4, No. 2, Spring 1990.

"The Real World of Malpractice Tort Reform," *Journal of Health and Hospital Law,* Vol. 23, Nos. 11/12, Nov. & Dec. 1990.

"An Interview with H. Charles Abbott" and "A Personal History of California Hospital Insurance Programs" in *Fifty Years – An Anthology by Ten Contributors who Helped Shape the History of California Hospitals,* January 1, 1991.

"Problems and Potentials of an Incremental Approach to Healthcare Access," Discussion Paper, June 13, 1991.

"Using Malpractice Claims Data to Successfully Attack the Problem of Infant Brain Damage," *Legal Medicine,* 1991.

"Reforming the Tort System," in *Treatise on Healthcare Law,* Vol. 3, 1991, updated 1996 (Matthew, Bender & Co.)

"Medical Malpractice Environment in the 1990s," *Medical Staff Counselor,* Vol. 6, No. 3, Summer 1992.

"A Charter for Healthcare Restructuring to Maintain and Improve the Healthcare Status of All Americans in a Cost-Effective Manner," submitted to Gail R. Wilensky, Ph.D., deputy assistant to the president, July 14, 1992.

"Healthcare Law, A Future Issues Agenda," paper, Conference on Legal Medicine, American College of Legal Medicine, March 8, 1996.

"Managed Care – Arbitration and Tort Reform," *QID Newsletter,* November 1996.

"The Changing Face of Liability – Malpractice and Risk Management in a Managed-care Environment," *California Medicine,* July 1997.

Index

Health Policy – The Hard Way

Health Policy – The Hard Way

Health Policy – The Hard Way

Additional copies of this book may be obtained
from your local bookstore,
or by sending $16.95 per copy
plus $3 postage/handling

to:

**Hope Publishing House
P.O. Box 60008
Pasadena, CA 91116**

CA residents please add 8¼% sales tax
FAX orders to: (626) 792-2121
Telephone VISA/MC orders to (800) 326-2671
E-mail orders to: hopepub@loop.com
Visit our Web site: http://www.hope-pub.com